THE
INVENTIONS
OF
LEONARDO
DA VINCI

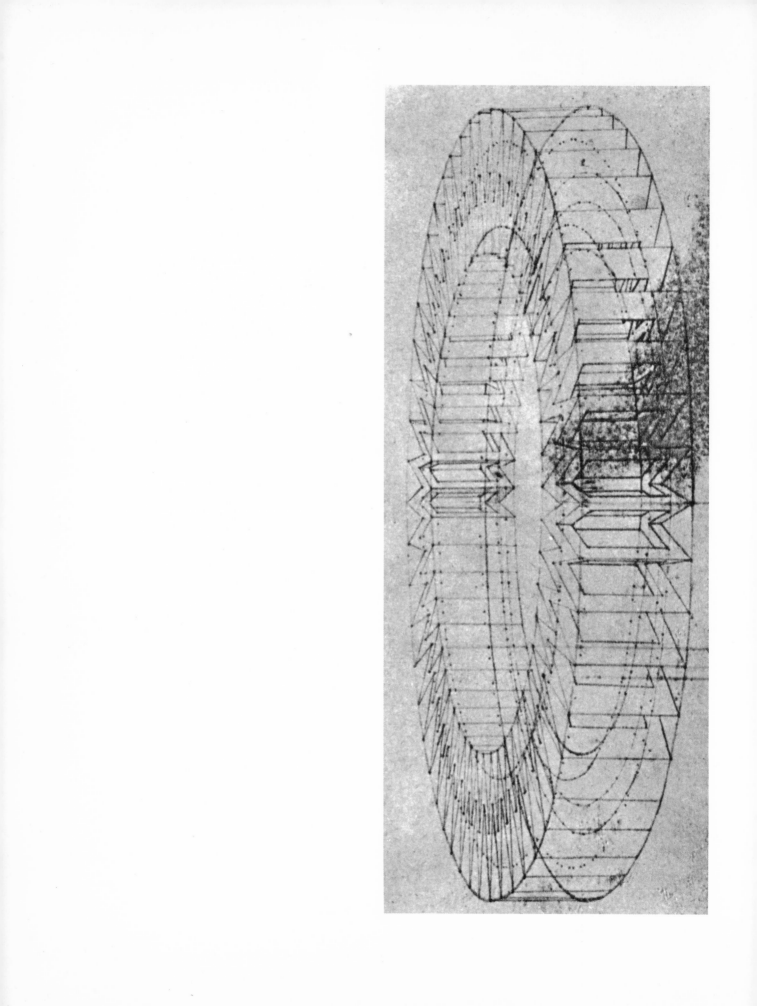

THE INVENTIONS OF LEONARDO DA VINCI

MARGARET COOPER

THE MACMILLAN COMPANY · NEW YORK

Library of Congress catalog card number: 65-13592
Title page illustration: Study of a water wheel by
Leonardo da Vinci (Codex Atlanticus 263r-a)
The Macmillan Company, New York
Collier-Macmillan Canada, Ltd., Toronto, Ontario
Printed in the United States of America
Third Printing, 1967

ACKNOWLEDGMENTS

We live in a time when our knowledge of the world around us is expanding at a dizzying rate, and none of us can hope to learn more than a little of what happens even in one field of science. In Leonardo's time, five hundred years ago, things were so different that the very foundations of modern science had not been laid. Galileo had yet to turn his telescope to the sky, Newton to sit under the famous apple tree, Copernicus to move man's earth from the center of the universe, Vesalius to reveal the structure of man himself. Leonardo, living as he did at the dawn of science, and working entirely alone, nevertheless observed, thought, and wrote on a range of scientific subjects that call for a whole group of modern specialists to explain. I have been most fortunate in receiving advice from many such specialists; they very kindly answered questions and supplied information about aspects of Leonardo's technical work I could not otherwise have dealt with. Their help has been both generous and indispensable.

First let me thank Mr. Jean Stock Goldstone, a nonspecialist, whose combined knowledge of Leonardo in particular and science in general was uniquely helpful to all sections of this book. Special thanks are due also to staff members of International Business Machines Corporation who provided facts on several subjects as well as pictures of models in the well-known IBM exhibit on Leonardo's inventions. Richard Collins, T. G. Delaney, Robert Monahon, Herbert Pedersen, W. R. Pitt, and Miss Lee Protzman have all been of great help.

For assistance with particular topics and inventions, I am indebted to all the following people and organizations: American Bridge Division, United States Steel Corporation; The American Museum-Hayden Planetarium; Professor E. Kenneth Bates, Jr., Maplewood High; Burton Dezendorf, American Optical Company; Dennis Duveen; Professor James Fitch, Columbia University; Hank Frey; Dr. Roberto Guatelli; Seth Hiller, architect; I. J. Karassik and E. F. Wright, Worthington Corporation; Captain William G. Kay; Dr. David Kimmelman; Bernard Krainis; James Lawson, Riverside Church; Claude Marks; D. J. McEachern, Standard Oil Company; Professor Arthur Price, Fashion Institute of Technology; Revere Copper and Brass, Inc.; Ernest Rockwood, American Manufacturing Company, Inc.; The Singer Company, Inc.; Paul Trautvetter, Jo Mielziner Studio; Professor Christopher Tunnard, Yale University;

and Professor Felix A. Wallace, Cooper Union for the Advancement of Science and Art.

I also wish to thank staff members of the New York Public Library, especially those in the Art and Map divisions, and the information services of the United States Army, United States Navy, and United States Air Force. And Mrs. Vera Gewanter kindly translated for me many passages in Leonardo's notes.

Among the various books I consulted, several were of outstanding value both for general background on Leonardo and his period and for specific material and direct quotations of Leonardo's writings: *Leonardo da Vinci*, a collection of essays by specialists in all the major fields of his work, Reynal & Company, 1956; Kenneth Clark, *Leonardo da Vinci*, Penguin Books, Inc., 1963; Ivor B. Hart, *The World of Leonardo da Vinci*, The Viking Press, 1962; Edward MacCurdy, *The Notebooks of Leonardo da Vinci*, Harcourt, Brace & World, Inc., 1954; and J. P. Richter, editor, *The Literary Works of Leonardo da Vinci*, Oxford University Press, 1939.

For possible errors herein, I have only myself to thank.

All reproductions from Leonardo's notebooks, with the exceptions listed below, were provided through the courtesy of the New York Public Library: Art Library, Elmer Belt Library of Vinciana, pages 4, 9, 16, 24, 36, 59, 79, 83, 97 (bottom), 100 (bottom), 117, 152; Art Reference Bureau, 19 (Alinari-Bulloz); International Business Machines Corporation, 48, 65, 84, 106, 122 (top), 135 (top, right), 138, 143, 145, 163, 166, 171.

Photographs of the Codex Atlanticus on pages 41, 49, 51, 76, 78, 81, 86, 89, 102, 104, 115, 123, 126, 127, 144, 155, 156, 157, 161, 165 were taken by Eric Pollitzer.

The two views of the revolving stage on page 37, which originally appeared in the Autumn 1949 issue of *Art Quarterly Magazine*, are reproduced with the kind permission of Miss Kate Steinitz, Curator, Art Library, Elmer Belt Library of Vinciana.

TO TI AND CHACH

CONTENTS

INTRODUCTION 2

THE ARTS 22
Introduction/Figure sketches for "The Last Supper"
Studies for Sforza horse monument

MUSIC 26
Introduction/Key trumpet/Mechanical drum
Mechanical viol/Bell and hammer

STAGE 32
Introduction/Festival scaffold/Costumes/Revolving stage

ARCHITECTURE 38
Introduction/Church plan/Spindle-shaped city
Multiple stairs/Double-decker city

CONSTRUCTION 44
Introduction/Mortar-making tools *and* Levels
Strength-of-columns study/Wire-strength tester
Hoisting crane/Double crane/Ratchet jack *and* Screw jack

FLIGHT 52
Introduction/Glider study/Flying machine
Landing-gear study/Flying saucer/Parachute/Aerial screw

HOME 62
Introduction/Air-cooling machine/Automatic roasting spit
Oil lamp/Alarm clock/Soil borer/Stable

INDUSTRY 70

Introduction/Copper-strip roller/Cannon-stave shaper
Screw-thread cutter/Spinning wheel/Nap-raising machine
Nap-shearing machine/Cord twister/Monkey wrench
Lathe *and* Saw/File-groove cutter/Pipe borer (horizontal)
Pipe borer (vertical)/Printing press
Needle grinder/Coin stamper

MAPS 90

Introduction/City of Imola/Tuscany
Pontine Marshes/World

MEASURE 98

Introduction/Compasses/Odometer *and* Pedometer
Inclinometer/Magnetic dip board *and* Method
of measuring earth's radius/Magnetic compass
Hygrometer/Anemometer/Steam-expansion tester
Method of measuring distance to the sun
and Method of measuring earth's radius
Clock with minute and hour hands

OPTICS 112

Introduction/Mirror and lens grinders/Projector
Spectacles/Telescope

POWER 120

Introduction/Pulley block/Roller bearings
Sprocket chains/Friction transmission/Differential
transmission/Three-speed gear transmission/Weight-
driven motor/Helical gears/Band brake for millstone
Water turbine/Gunpowder piston/Air turbine

TRANSPORTATION 132

Introduction/Streamlined hulls/Paddle-wheel boat
Two-level bridge/Horseless wagon

WAR *140*

Introduction/Machine gun/Wheel-lock closure for
breech-loading cannon/Cannon lighter/Steam gun
Shrapnel/Mortars/Fin bomb/Swing bridges
Tank/Double-hull ship *and* "Mysterious vessel"
Hull borer *and* Diving suit/Undersea anchor
Circular fortress

WATER *158*

Introduction/Breathing tube/Webbed glove
Life preserver/Floating shoes *and* Method of raising
water by means of fire/Water-supply pump
Water-raising system/Conical valve/Centrifugal
pump/Well drill/Force pump with bellows
Floating dredge/Canal excavator/Canal plan *and*
Lock gates/Deluge

INDEX OF ILLUSTRATIONS *176*

GENERAL INDEX *177*

INTRODUCTION

"Though human ingenuity may make various inventions which, by the help of various machines, answer the same end, it will never devise invention more beautiful, nor more simple, nor more to the purpose than nature does; because in her inventions nothing is wanting and nothing is superfluous, and she needs no counterpoise when she makes limbs proper for motion in the bodies of animals."

On a warm August day in 1911, the world's most famous painting disappeared from the Louvre Museum, in Paris. All efforts by the police to locate the missing masterpiece were in vain: nobody could find a trace of it for more than two years, and people began to wonder whether it would ever be seen again. Finally the picture turned up in Florence, the city where the artist had painted it four centuries earlier. An Italian house painter named Vincenzo Perugia, possibly employed by a ring of underworld art dealers, had stolen it while helping to redecorate the Louvre. He kept the picture hidden for a time, then took it to Italy with the idea of selling it there. Naturally, the painting was recognized at once, and it was soon returned to the Louvre, where it hangs in a place of honor.

In his own lifetime, around the year 1500, the artist who created this unique portrait was considered almost a magician by people who saw it, so great was his skill. There was something mysteriously beautiful about the smile of the lady in the picture that made everyone stop and wonder what it meant. Hundreds of years later, people are still stopping and wondering.

Of course the mysteriously smiling lady was "Mona Lisa" by Leonardo da Vinci. And Leonardo himself was also mysterious; the haunting smile he gave "Mona Lisa" might have been his own.

Here was a man, tall and wonderfully handsome, strong enough to bend a horseshoe with his hands and gentle enough to buy caged birds so that he could give them their freedom. A man whose skill as a painter seemed so miraculous to others, yet never perfect enough to please himself. He would begin huge projects like trying to change the course of a river, but he would leave many of them unfinished. He could speak of war as "the most bestial madness," yet he could invent the most deadly weapons, perhaps hoping they would never be used. He refused to eat meat because he hated to have animals harmed, but he was willing to sketch a man being hanged. The same

Leonardo who tried to invent mechanical wings, to give men the grandeur of flight, could also take time out to write directions for making and setting off a stinkbomb!

And Leonardo's drawings show that he loved beauty and ugliness equally well. Again and again he drew the faces of lovely young men and women; just as often he drew the faces of the grotesque and hideous. He charmed all he spoke to, yet he kept himself apart, leading a solitary life and devoting himself to his unending studies. Here was truly a man of opposites. No wonder he seemed strange and mysterious to those who knew him.

Mysterious or no, Leonardo wanted to understand all he saw around him; he made the whole universe his field of study. A list of the subjects he investigated would have to include not only painting but architecture, mathematics, geology, and optics; botany, aviation, and engineering; music, astronomy, philosophy, mechanics, and so on. In an age of exploration, Leonardo was the boldest explorer of all. While his fellow countryman Christopher Columbus was discovering America, Leonardo was, in a sense, discovering the world. He stands out from his time as the first modern scientist, a man living in the fifteenth century, with twentieth-century ideas.

The desire to paint the inner truth about nature first led Leonardo to the study of science. Looking at one of his paintings, we feel as if the people in it have come to life in front of us and the plants are actually growing. The artist could achieve this amazing quality of life because he felt a special harmony with nature and all living things, from the most important man to the least important flower. He believed that a painter should put nature on his canvas and show people the truth: not just how things looked on the outside but how they really were. A painted dog, for example, should seem so real that another dog seeing it would bark. "Truth is so excellent," wrote Leonardo, "that if it praises but small things they become noble."

With his sharp eyes, deft hands, and brilliant mind, Leonardo unlocked many of nature's secrets, investigating the structure of mountains, learning much about the human body, and examining every kind of animal and plant. Picture him as a tall, wavy-haired boy, roaming the mountains around the town of Vinci, where he was born, and studying the flying birds for hours at a time or watching every bubble and current in a mountain stream. Or picture him later in life as a dignified and elegant bearded man, burning his lamp far into the night in a workroom crammed with plant specimens and

(Introduction continued on page 5)

LEONARDO MAY HAVE BEEN THE MODEL for this statue of David as a young man by Andrea del Verrocchio. During his first years in Florence, Leonardo worked in Verrocchio's studio. There he developed his art and his science, because Verrocchio worked both as artist and engineer, a common arrangement at that time. Most people believe that Leonardo posed for the statue during this period, and the face seems to correspond with descriptions of him in his youth. However, a specialist at the Metropolitan Museum of Art, in New York City, believes that Leonardo was the sculptor rather than the model; he explains that the statue's style and ornament look more like the work of Leonardo than like that of Verrocchio. Perhaps it was a youthful self-portrait.

Verrocchio's real name was Andrea di Michele di Francesco di Cioni; he came to be known as Verrocchio, meaning "true eye," because he was admired for the accuracy of his work. Leonardo's name of course, means that he came from the town of Vinci.

machine parts, animal bones and rocks, and immense stacks of papers covered with his notes and drawings on every possible subject.

Another man might have studied nature just enough to find out what he needed to know for his painting. But not Leonardo. He had not only endless skill and endless patience, but endless curiosity as well. He always wanted to know the reason why, and some of the questions he asked himself had never been asked before. His thirst for learning was so great that he called knowledge the "mother of love" and impatience the "mother of stupidity." So he tried to learn everything, often putting aside his art for months at a time in favor of his science. And since his way of looking at nature was part of his extraordinary genius, he seldom missed a thing. When Leonardo looked at a whirlpool or a flying bird, he tried to use his eyes like a slow-motion camera. Combining his almost superhuman eyesight and his analytical way of using it, he could see and remember swift movements that would be invisible to others, and guess at the inner structure from looking at the surface. The proof of his unusual achievements as an observer exists in his drawings, which show details of moving water not pictured again until the invention of photography.

Besides his wish to paint truthfully and his love of knowledge, Leonardo had another incentive for making his scientific studies. During the fifteenth century, when he lived, artists often worked for princes and dukes, who commissioned them to paint portraits of important people at court and pictures to beautify churches and palaces. Leonardo's magnificent fresco, "The Last Supper," painted on the wall of a Milan church, is an example of such a picture. Painting, however, was only one of their duties: as servants of the court, artists were also expected to plan and direct pageants to amuse the courtiers, creating the costumes, props, and scenery, and to assist in designing buildings and weapons for defense. Often a prince was only as strong as his castle and the walls of the city where it stood; if he couldn't defend it, his power ended. Leonardo worked for many years at the court of Ludovico Sforza, Duke of Milan, who frequently called upon him to do anything from devising a heating system for the Duchess' bath water to improving a fortress. In fact, the Duke valued Leonardo equally as an artistic genius and master of engineering. True to character, Leonardo carried his duties as engineer far beyond the immediate practical needs, into a deep study of mechanics.

Luckily, Leonardo lived at the right time to make the most of his studies. He was born into the Renaissance, an age when men in Italy began taking a new look at the world. For hundreds of years, people had been content to believe that nearly everything in nature was arranged for the glory of God, and there was little need to ask questions about its mysteries. They lived on the land in small groups that took care of themselves; their place in life never changed and they saw no reason for the world to change either.

We all know that the world changes whether people see a reason for it or not. Little by little, small towns became rich, powerful cities, and people felt less tied to the land. Merchants began trading in faraway places, coming home with fragrant spices, gorgeous silks, and strange tales of their travels. By the time of Leonardo's birth, in 1452, Florence had grown to a thriving city of a hundred thousand people, its streets lined with splendid stone houses, churches, and busy shops. Arriving there as a country boy from nearby Vinci at the age of sixteen, Leonardo stepped into a new and beautiful world, full of color and music and wise conversation. Instead of living mainly to hope for the delights of Heaven when they died, as their forefathers had done in centuries past, people were enjoying their life on earth as well. And instead of their old dependence on feudal lord and church, they were beginning to make choices for themselves. Because making choices brings a need for knowledge of the world, the stage was set for a new scene.

In 1453, when Leonardo was one year old, the Turks drove out the Greeks who had long ruled Constantinople. Some of these Greeks came to Italy, and they brought with them precious copies of ancient writings by great men of classic Greek science. The use of the recently invented printing press made possible wider distribution of these books and others; thus began the intense revival of scientific learning in Italy. Once men began to study nature again, they wanted to know more and more. They still believed, as most people do now, that only God could create the perfect harmony of nature, but they also had a new faith in their own power to control nature by learning its laws. Therefore they not only mastered the science of ancient times but went on to make new discoveries of their own.

If Leonardo, who died in 1519, had lived a century earlier, he might not have had either the desire or the chance to study science as he did, nor would he have had so much of the ancient Greek knowledge to guide him. Even in his own time, many superstitious people misunderstood what he was trying to do as a scientist, and

THE STAR OF BETHLEHEM, a hardy spring lily, might almost be
growing in this sketch. Leonardo understood so well the structure
of plants that he knew how to show the intricacies of the leaves and
flowers in sketches that became works of art rather than mere technical drawings. As an artist concerned with landscape painting, he
also took special care to study how the light falls on trees, and the
delicate color shadings of leaves. Leonardo not only included detailed
landscapes in the background of such paintings as "Mona Lisa," but
he is said to have drawn the first landscape without figures known in
European art.

suspected him of dealing in black magic. He met with his greatest difficulties in his attempts to learn about the structure of the human body. The church considered the bodies of the dead sacred, and disapproved so strongly of dissection that in the end Leonardo had to give up his pioneering work in anatomy.

This kind of suspicion may or may not explain why he wrote all his notes backward; to read his handwriting you have to hold the paper up to a mirror. It is true that Leonardo was left-handed, and he may have found it easier—or it may have amused him—to write from right to left. Nevertheless, he had been taught to write the way other people do, so there must have been more to it than that. The mirror writing certainly would have discouraged most people from trying to read his notes before he was ready to publish them himself, as he eventually planned. Perhaps it also protected his unusual ideas from being stolen. Or perhaps, as many believe, the secrecy of his nature led him to write that way.

The son of a Florentine notary, Leonardo had little formal education. Most boys didn't go to school then, and few people had private tutors. He did learn some mathematics as a boy, and, like many brilliant men, he gained an excellent grasp of the reasoning but was bad at arithmetic—his notes show examples like multiplying 5 times 16 and getting a result of 60. Later on, he taught himself enough Latin so that he could read books on the many subjects that interested him.

ONE FIGURE IN TWO POSITIONS illustrates typical human proportions. "The span of a man's outstretched arms is equal to his height," Leonardo wrote, and drew a square around the figure to emphasize his point. Explaining the circle, he noted, "If you set your legs so far apart as to take a fourteenth part from your height, and you open and raise your arms until you touch the line of the crown of the head with your middle fingers, you must know that the center of the circle formed by the extremities of the outstretched limbs will be the navel, and the space between the legs will form an equilateral triangle."

As part of his anatomy studies, Leonardo made detailed measurements of bodily proportions, from head to toe, but he didn't necessarily use his own findings when he painted figures. He believed that if a painter gave every figure the same proportions, all people in his paintings would look alike, and this effect would not be true to nature.

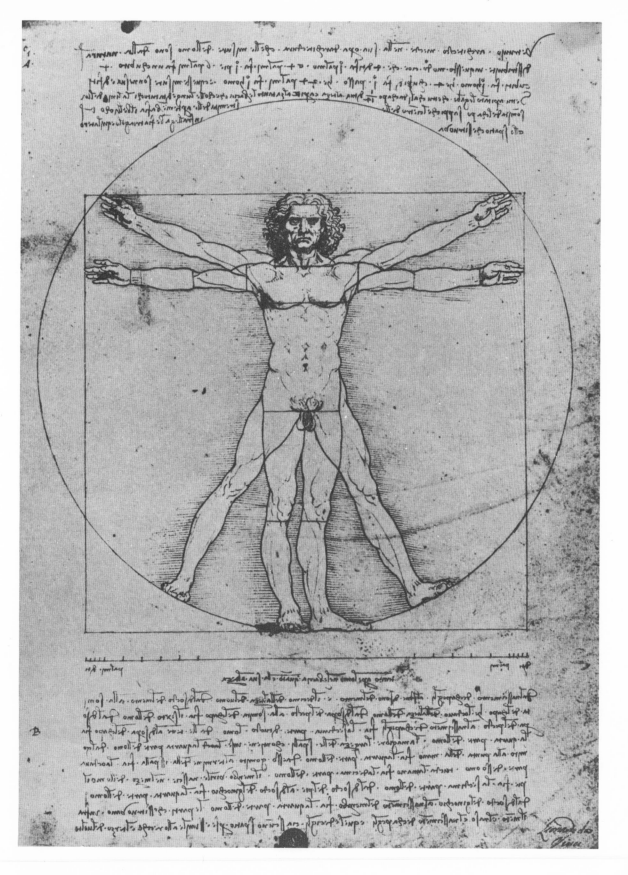

But if Leonardo didn't know his multiplication tables so well, he understood very well indeed the importance of mathematics as a science with definite answers to questions. He anticipated, by 125 years, Galileo's famous statement that "the book of nature is written in numbers." He always insisted on following strict mathematical rules to test the truth of his ideas, and he believed that any worthwhile scientific idea should be able to stand the test. Beyond even his most logical proofs, however, Leonardo had an almost uncanny ability to sense the truth, and this intuition helped him to a knowledge of many facts not officially discovered until much later. For example, he watched how the wind ripples the top of a field of grain while the bottom remains still: "The May wind moves like a wave in the grain, and the wave is seen to travel over the field, and the stalks of grain do not move from their place." He realized that waves move the same way on water, going over the surface and leaving the water below undisturbed.

Then his intuition took him an amazing step further. Just as water moves in waves, he decided, so do light and sound. He illustrated this idea by showing how two pebbles dropped into the water a little distance apart make widening circles on the surface. As these circles become larger, they cross each other without merging or changing their shape; each set of circles continues to grow, unaffected by the other. The sound from two bells travels exactly the same way, he believed, and that's why you can hear them clearly and separately, although one may be farther from you than the other.

Still thinking along the same lines, Leonardo stated, "Every body gives off rays." By a "body," he didn't mean just a human body, but any mass of matter from a rock to a skunk, or even the sun. And depending on what the body is, the rays, or waves, may be light or

Two CIRCULAR RIPPLES CROSS WITHOUT BREAKING, said Leonardo, because a ripple on the water's surface reflects the shock to the water of something dropped in one spot. As the water in that spot immediately returns to its place, the shock moves out in all directions and can be seen as widening rings. Leonardo extended this idea of shock waves radiating outward to explain the movement of sound and light. "Water struck by water makes circles around the spot struck," he wrote. "For a longer distance, the voice within the air. Longer within fire. Further the mind within the universe; but as it is finite, it cannot embrace the infinite."

sound, heat, magnetism, or odor. That is to say, the rock may give off rays of heat that travel in expanding circles like the ripples in the pool; the sun gives off rays of light; and the skunk, rays of odor. Imagine the mind of a man who can look at what happens when he throws pebbles into the water and guess, from what he sees, an important truth about the invisible movements of nature!

He went to the tops of the mountains in the countryside near Florence and saw the fossils of sea creatures in the rocks. While other people in his day thought the fossils had been left by the Flood, when God caused the waters to rise and cover even the mountains, Leonardo imagined the changes of the earth through the ages, and he wrote, "What was once the bottom of the sea has become the top of the mountains." And he showed that the mountains had been formed in layers and that some of the fossils were older than others.

In still another study, his remarkable vision apparently showed him that the speed of a falling weight increases as it falls, and his remarkable intuition told him what he couldn't possibly have seen: that the movement of the earth turning pulls a falling weight slightly to one side. While this knowledge was of no use to Leonardo, it is of great importance now for the proper launching and recovery of spaceships.

Leonardo had many ideas that we think of as recent. Four centuries before the invention of radio, and long before international postal service, he said, "Men from the most remote countries shall speak to one another and shall reply." He invented a workable parachute, and he knew the principle of the telescope, as he proved in a note he wrote reminding himself, "Make glasses to magnify the moon." He also claimed he had invented a "mysterious vessel," probably something like a submarine; he kept the design a secret, however, fearing that it would be too destructive. But even more modern than these startling ideas and inventions was Leonardo's approach to science. It is this approach that earns him the right to be called the first modern scientist.

For Leonardo, as for us, the scientific approach began with observation: watching the movements of water, the path of a dropping fruit or leaf, the flight of a bird, the shape of the clouds. By carefully observing such things as these, much can be learned about the workings of nature. A bird watcher, for example, learns how to distinguish birds and bird families not only by their color and size but also by the shape of their beaks, the way they fly, their songs and their habits. The bird watcher is doing on a limited scale what the scientist also does: observing with an eye to finding the *significant facts*.

Leonardo extended bird watching to everything he could see; he was a nature watcher. He had a rare talent for knowing which facts were significant and how facts about one aspect of nature could be connected with parallel facts about another aspect. Speaking of the wind, he said, "The air moves like a river and carries the clouds with it; just as running water carries all the things that float upon it." He went on to explain that if the wind blew through the air and drove the clouds from behind rather than floating them, the clouds would be squeezed by the resistance of the air in front and the moving force of the wind behind, like "wax pressed between the fingers." In this short note, Leonardo made three observations: he noticed the clouds carried through the sky by the wind; he related this action of moving air to a similar action of water; and he gave an illustration of invisible air pressures in terms of a visible human action. Thus he searched for the significant fact about the way the wind moves and carries clouds, and tried to explain it by comparison.

Direct observation of nature often needs another kind of observation to verify it. This second kind of observation is experiment: setting up a controlled test to imitate the pattern of nature and isolate one feature of this pattern. We can directly observe that ripe fruit always falls to the ground from its tree and never rises into the air. But if we want to find out whether a large, heavy fruit falls faster than a small, light one, we need to create an artificial set of conditions retaining the essential features of nature. A popular story tells us that Galileo made such a test by simultaneously dropping a light and a heavy object from the top of the Leaning Tower of Pisa; when the two objects landed at about the same moment, he had demonstrated that the speed of their fall had not been affected by the difference in their weight. If this test and its result seems obvious to us, we shall do well to remember that no one before Galileo ever discovered this significant fact about falling objects.

Galileo, and Leonardo before him, recognized that observation and experiment must be repeated many times before they may serve as a basis for making a general rule, or theory, about an action of nature. Galileo was born in 1564; seventy years later, well into the seventeenth century, he had to answer to the Inquisition for his theory that the sun, not the earth, is the center of our universe. Contrary to what happens in today's world ruled by science, finding out about nature for yourself and having your own theories were not encouraged in Galileo's or Leonardo's day. People believed that you could simply read what the ancient Greeks said or what the Bible said about nature, and that settled it. Leonardo had deep respect for the ancient Greeks and the Bible, but he still thought their theories should be tested. "Anyone who argues by referring to authority is not using his mind but rather his memory," he wrote. Five hundred years ago, that was a very bold statement for a scientist to make.

"THIS ANIMAL WITH ITS RESOUNDING ROAR rouses its cubs on the third day after their birth and teaches them the use of all their dormant senses, and all the wild creatures in the forest flee away.

"One may liken these to the children of virtue who are wakened by the sound of praise: their studies grow in distinction, raising them continually more and more, and at the sound all that is evil flees away, shunning those who are virtuous."

Leonardo often drew morals of this sort from his observations of nature, applying the behavior of animals to human problems. He also wrote many fables and prophecies; sometimes he presented them as riddles. "Men shall cast away their own food," he wrote, meaning that in springtime peasants would sow seeds in the ground. Or, "The forests will bring forth young who will become the cause of their death," referring to ax handles made of wood. For the most part, Leonardo dwelt on gloomy possibilities, but in one of his happiest prophecies he said, "Feathers shall raise men towards heaven even as they do birds:—that is, by letters written with their quills."

Like the men of science who came after him, Leonardo wanted to make tests in order to prove or disprove general ideas that explain such specific happenings as fruit dropping from a tree. He believed that every happening in nature can be explained by a basic reason, or law; and he believed that once you can establish the basic reason you can stop testing each case. If you know that gravity draws weight to the ground, you know also that not only will fruit drop but water will spill from an overturned glass, and that you will return quickly to earth when you jump into the air. However, it takes a person like Leonardo or Galileo to be the first to think about gravity as an explanation for falling objects: such a person must have the scientific insight to see the connection between many separate events. "Theory is the captain and practice the foot soldiers," Leonardo wrote; and he experimented with separate cases until he thought he had found a general rule to explain them.

During years of experiment with objects set in motion, he made notes indicating a general theory: "Force is . . . an invisible power which is implanted by accidental violence in all bodies that are withheld from their natural inclination"; "it transforms and constrains every body with change of position and form"; "weight changes unwillingly and force is always on the point of fleeing." In these comments and others, Leonardo was discussing inertia, the reason why a body "changes unwillingly," whether at rest or in motion, and needs an outside force to start or stop it. The body may be a revolving door that has to be pushed harder to start moving than to keep going, or it may be a ball that hits the hand hard when you catch it because you have stopped the motion that would otherwise have continued. Either way, by starting the revolving door that was at rest or by stopping the ball that was in motion, you are overcoming the resistance of inertia.

Almost two centuries after Leonardo made his study, Sir Isaac Newton thought about the same problem and wrote his first law of motion: "Every body persists in a state of rest or of uniform motion in a straight line, unless compelled by external forces to change that state." Newton was the first person to make a clear and formal statement about this fact of nature, and to publish it for others to learn, but Leonardo was first to discover the great importance of inertia and how it affects motion.

Though Leonardo could look so far into the future and dream of it vividly, he was also a practical man. He sought to discover the laws of nature partly because he believed that each action of nature has a useful purpose. In the midst of his deep, abstract studies, he often made notes to himself like this one: "When you write of the motions of water, remember to put under each proposition its uses, that this science may not be useless." Again following his own advice, he drew on his knowledge of nature's actions to make the numerous machines he designed as useful as possible.

From boyhood, Leonardo had a natural understanding of machinery and a natural interest in designing it. As an apprentice to Andrea del Verrocchio, a noted Florentine painter, sculptor, goldsmith, and mechanical craftsman, Leonardo increased his practical knowledge of the design and structure of machinery. Some of his earliest sketches showed machine parts and how they worked. With more experience, he developed a new attitude to solving problems of machine design: while most people of the period thought of each machine as different, because each was doing its own special job, Leonardo recognized that the real point was not whether a machine wound thread or stamped out coins, but why and how it operated. For instance, he knew that linking a small gear to a larger one reduces speed and increases power, and he applied this one idea successfully to machines as different as a hoisting crane and a copper-strip roller. By getting to the basic function as he did, he could use a few general rules to improve or invent many machines for all sorts of jobs. Leonardo's mastery of machinery went so far beyond the understanding of most other men that some mistook his knowledge for magic.

The first purpose of a machine, of course, is to save labor, and as soon as we begin talking about labor, or effort, we're talking about power, the moving force of machines.

Most of our present-day machines take advantage of two kinds of modern power: electricity and the internal-combustion engine; but their introduction was centuries away when Leonardo did his work. Besides the muscles of people and draft animals, the only kinds of power available to him were air, water, weight, and springs. The natural motion of wind and running water, the natural fall of a weight, or the natural release of a spring can all be used to turn a wheel or do other similar work. Of these, water was by far the most useful in fifteenth-century Italy because it turned water wheels to make some processes, like grinding flour, automatic. Leonardo carefully studied the possibilities of all four power sources—and considered new ones—and how to use them to best advantage, increasing the work they could do by means of efficient transmission

(Introduction continued on page 17)

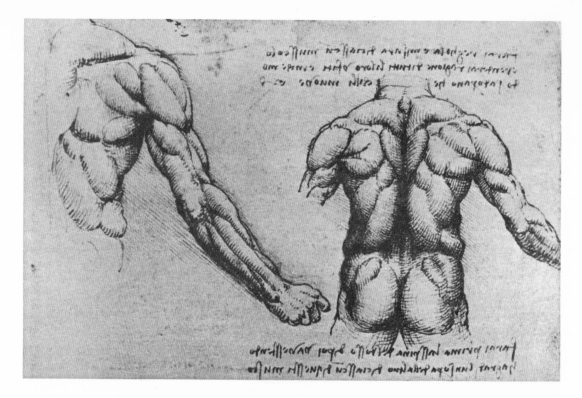

"YOU WILL MAKE THE RULE AND THE MEASUREMENT of each muscle," Leonardo instructed himself, "and you will give the reason of all their functions, and the manner in which they use them and who moves them."

This drawing typifies the keen observation and outstanding draftsmanship that Leonardo brought to his studies of anatomy, among the first such studies ever made; the note he wrote is typical of his modern approach to the subject. He was not satisfied simply to observe and to draw, but always sought to learn the function of each part of the body as a key to its structure, because he believed that "the Creator does not make anything superfluous or defective." His thorough investigation of the human body, based on many dissections, dealt with nerve systems and bone structure, as well as the heart, the eye, and other important organs, and he studied both men and women.

In his notes on the body, Leonardo also had a word for doctors: "Strive to preserve your health; and in this you will the better succeed as you keep clear of physicians, for their drugs are a kind of alchemy concerning which there are no fewer books than there are medicines." It is an interesting comment about the medical ideas of a period when prescriptions included everything from ground toads to ground diamonds.

systems. Thus a little power could do a big job. He used gears to increase power, as in the crane, and also to make power go further; we use gears this way, for example, in a wrist watch, where one spring can turn several gears.

Nearly five centuries ago, by means of springs and gears Leonardo actually invented a self-propelling wagon that needed no horse to pull it. He combined gears with a falling weight to make one of the first clocks that could measure minutes as well as hours, and with the water wheel he made a well pump, using the same stream as a source of both supply and power. Frequently he also made use of the lever and the pulley, two other means to lift extra weight and extend power. Leonardo's inventions seem all the more astounding when we realize what he did with such limited power sources. Indeed, their remarkable efficiency proves that even in the fifteenth century it was possible for a forward-looking man to think in terms of automation.

Tools for making accurate measurements were also limited in Leonardo's time. There were no really reliable instruments for measuring speeds or distances, either on land or at sea, for measuring the force of the wind or the moisture in the air or the amount of rainfall. Nor did proper tools exist for measuring the angles between earth and stars, angles so important to navigation. We have to marvel at how Columbus managed to cross a huge, unknown ocean, having so little help to keep him on his course. For example, his astrolabe, the disc used to measure star angles, was so large and heavy that three people were needed to work it: one to hold it, one to set the pointer, and one to read what it said. With such a clumsy instrument, mistakes are almost bound to happen.

Just as we need exact measurements for navigation, we need them for construction. Even so simple a structure as a box depends on measurement for good results: the more exactly its length on each side and the angles of its corners can be measured, the better it will fit together and the more useful it will be. The same holds true for buildings and complicated machines; in fact, the more complicated they are, the more necessary it becomes for all the measurements of size and weight to be perfect.

Once again Leonardo, the universal man, plunged in and invented a variety of measuring tools: not only his clock to measure time more precisely, but a scale that made it easier to read weights, an instrument to attach to a wagon wheel to measure the distance the wagon traveled, and several others, including instruments to measure the weather. In this important area, as in so many others, Leonardo was far ahead of his times. Since science can be only as exact as its measurements, some people even judge the whole progress of science by the progress of measuring tools. Our present-day instruments, delicate enough to measure in millionths of inches or seconds, reflect the advanced stage of modern science.

Leonardo had a special interest in measuring because he strove for perfection in both art and science. He called science "the knowledge of things possible in the future, of the present and of the past," and he tried to know all three. By his own definition there is no doubt that Leonardo was a great scientist. He mastered the science of the past, improved both the practical and theoretical science of his own time, and, with his amazing intuition, foresaw many of the things possible in the future even up to the present day.

We know of his work, his inventions, and his brilliant guesses because he kept notebooks: thousands of pages covered with his small mirror writing and his strikingly beautiful drawings. He wrote down and drew his thoughts and ideas just as they occurred to him, moving swiftly from one subject to another. Everything, no matter how small, was important enough to be noted. On a single page you might find a sketch of a horse, notes on pulleys, and a list of household expenses.

Leonardo's notebooks can now be seen in various museums and private collections of Europe. Actually, what we call "notebooks" were in some cases exactly that and in others loose sheets of paper, collected into notebooks long after Leonardo's time. In his will, Leonardo provided that all his notes should belong to a young pupil of his, Francesco Melzi, who stayed with him during his last years in France. For reasons no one has ever understood, Melzi paid little attention to the notes, and apparently valued them little, too. The notes were gradually dispersed, beginning in Melzi's lifetime and continuing thereafter, into the hands of private collectors who wanted them because of Leonardo's fame as an artist; they didn't find it worth the trouble to figure out what the notes said. Much later, the notes were assembled into notebooks and given titles. For example, the Codex Atlanticus, the largest and most important of all the collections, gets its name because, like the Atlantic Ocean, it is very large. This codex is in a Milan library, while other manuscripts, called MS A, MS B, and so on, are in the Institute of France, in Paris. Still other notebooks and drawings, such as the Codex Leicester, the Codex Arundel, and the Windsor collection, are in

"LEONARDO DYING IN THE ARMS OF FRANCIS I," by the nineteenth-century French painter Jean-Auguste-Dominique Ingres, carries forward a legend, begun by one of Leonardo's first biographers, that the King of France was present during the artist's last hours. While the story contradicts the facts, it is true that Leonardo spent his final years, from 1516 to 1519, in the service of the French king, and lived at Amboise, where he is buried. It is also true that Francis I esteemed him greatly for his wisdom and knowledge. According to Benvenuto Cellini, who spent some time in France, "I must not fail to repeat the words spoken of him by the King, who said to me . . . that he believed no other man had been born into the world who knew as much as Leonardo—not so much speaking of sculpture, painting and architecture, as saying that he was a very great philosopher."

When Leonardo went to France, he took with him several paintings, including "Mona Lisa"; his departure from his native Italy explains why this portrait hangs in the Louvre.

England; the Leicester and Arundel manuscripts are named for the English earls who originally acquired them. In some notebooks, such as the small one in Turin, Italy, dealing with the flight of birds, Leonardo kept mainly to one subject, but for the most part the notebooks cover many topics at random.

Because Leonardo kept his records in such a jumble, finding out what he had to say on any one subject usually resembles a treasure hunt: one must follow the clues on hundreds of pages to discover his thoughts. If this lack of arrangement seems exasperating, we must remember that he didn't intend anyone but himself to read his notes. He had plans for putting together the scattered notes on each subject and writing scientific books about everything from flight and anatomy to rock formations and canals. It is not surprising that he never found the time to carry out his plans.

Nor is it surprising, under the circumstances, that Leonardo's discoveries and inventions do not receive mention in many science books and that most people know him as a great artist, but few know of his equally dramatic work in science. Since he never wrote the books he planned, only his disorganized mirror-writing notes remained to tell the world about what he accomplished; it wasn't until the last hundred years or so that anyone really began to examine them carefully. Though he was first to think of many scientific ideas, the world didn't benefit by them until other men made the same discoveries, sometimes centuries later, and published books about them.

Today, as the possibilities he foresaw are becoming realities, we are learning the full extent of his thoughts. We are learning, too, that such a many-sided genius as he has probably never lived before or since in the whole history of the world. We know now that Leonardo was not only the first to think of a streamlined ship but the first to draw an accurate picture of the human heart and describe its action; not only the first to think of the helicopter for human flight but the first to understand the way leaves are arranged around the stems of plants; not only the first to invent a diving suit with an air reservoir but the first to explain that it was not the eye alone which divides light into the colors of the rainbow. He was not only the first to draw maps giving an idea of the hills and valleys in the landscape but may possibly have been the first to draw a world map showing the name "America." This one man, a man who lived a solitary life, detached from human concerns, observed, thought, and wrote so much that we can hardly understand how he did it.

And because Leonardo could draw with such marvelous skill, his contribution to science is unique twice over. His drawings of machinery are so clear and accurate that they might be shop plans for workmen to follow; in a well-known collection of models built from his sketches, all the machines work perfectly. No anatomical drawings have ever surpassed those of his which show a part of the body from all sides to illustrate how it functions. His drawings of moving water have a completeness of detail that even modern photography can hardly improve upon.

By his close study of nature, Leonardo made art a science. By his inner sense of beauty and form, he made science an art. Perhaps it is this wonderful combination of seeing and feeling, of knowing and imagining that shines through the smile of "Mona Lisa" and makes her the most admired and mysterious woman in the world.

THIS STUDY OF HANDS shows that Leonardo not only ranked as an inspired draftsman but also had a detailed knowledge of anatomy. In drawing people, as in all his drawing and painting, Leonardo believed that the artist must understand the inner workings and spirit of his subject to be able to make a proper picture of its outer surface. It was this approach to art that gave him the remarkable power to make his painted subjects seem alive. The hands in Leonardo's painting of "Mona Lisa" impressed one little girl so much that she said, "The beauty of her hands stands out like jewels."

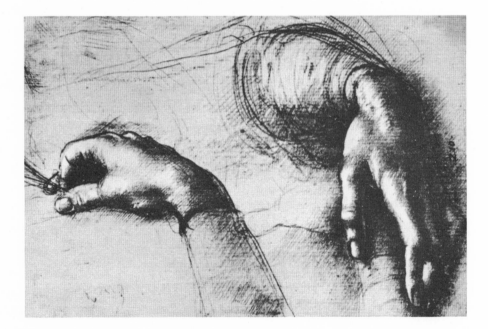

THE ARTS

"The painter can call into being the essence of animals of all kinds, of plants, fruits, landscapes, rolling plains, crumbling mountains, fearful and terrible places which strike terror into the spectator; and again pleasant places, sweet and delightful with meadows of many-colored flowers bent by the gentle motion of the wind which turns back to look at them as it floats on."

It would be interesting to know what style Leonardo would choose as a present-day painter. Would he be a realist or a surrealist? an impressionist, an expressionist, or a cubist? Or would he be another Picasso, with a wide variety of styles and subjects? Leonardo lived in such a different age that it's hard to imagine him painting in any of our modern styles. One can much more readily visualize him as a twentieth-century scientist: our objective approach to the sciences comes far closer to his attitude than our very personal approach to the arts.

When Leonardo began to paint, the whole world of nature had recently become an absorbing subject for artists to observe and interpret, and the art of the Greeks and Romans had become a new influence too. For the first time in centuries, painters had turned their attention from the symbolism of church art to the realism of everyday life. Where faces and trees, for example, had before been idealized into general types, painters of Leonardo's period wanted also to deal with a face or a tree as an individual. Portraiture and landscape painting were both new ideas, and their introduction came gradually. At first a painter might select a traditional religious subject like the Adoration of the Magi, but give the kings the faces of important living people, thus blending the old ideas with the new. To Leonardo, the world of people and nature had so many wonders that he found no reason to turn his mind inward, as many painters do now, for ideas or moods to paint. He believed that "the mind of the painter should be like a mirror which always takes the color of the thing it reflects, and which is filled by as many images as there are things placed before it."

Nor was the Renaissance an age of specialization like ours, with a sharp division between art and science. Through applying mathematics to painting problems, Leonardo and others worked out the laws of perspective, a new discovery. Anatomy and the proportions of the human figure also occupied Leonardo's attention, and with oil paints, then new in Italy, he evolved the misty quality called *sfumato*, which helps give the impression that figures in a painting are placed in three-dimensional space. He was one of the first to convey the shadings of inner feeling by positions of the hands, facial expressions, and general attitudes of his painted figures. "The Last Supper" owes much of its great fame to this achievement. Leonardo wrote a whole treatise on painting, giving advice on everything from how to draw and how to deal with drapery to how aerial perspective should be created by scientific shading of the color. Supposedly, he himself used a set of measuring spoons for mixing exact color tones, but he didn't always follow his own theoretical advice, probably because inspiration often begins where reasoning leaves off.

In the fifteenth century, painting was just one of the activities of artists like Leonardo. Both Leonardo and Michelangelo were concerned with military affairs, designing fortifications, and most artists of the time had theories about architecture. Besides all that, many served as festival directors, a duty that required talent as scenery- and costume-designer and lighting expert, as well as a taste for magic effects.

If you find it hard to understand why great Renaissance artists had so many different duties, remember that the time was not long past when an artist, no matter how great, was thought of simply as a wonderfully gifted craftsman: not really an artist but an artisan. We know very little, for instance, of the geniuses who designed the great cathedrals of Europe and created the marvelous stained glass, statuary, and carvings that adorn them. Living as he did in a threshold period, when artists were still artisans as well, Leonardo received great praise for his unique vision and skill, but he was also expected to undertake many projects apart from his painting. Typically, he threw himself into each of these projects and more, and just as typically, he left many of them unfinished. ✠

FIGURE SKETCHES FOR "THE LAST SUPPER," Leonardo's great mural in the church of Santa Maria delle Grazie in Milan, appear on the same sheet with an instrument called a hygrometer, designed "to know the qualities and density of the air, and when it is going to rain." It is not an accident that art and science go together here. Because Leonardo disliked working as quickly as fresco-painting technique in wet plaster requires, he devised a technique of his own for more leisurely work on "The Last Supper." He wanted to know how much moisture was in the air, because dampness affected his method of painting, and the hygrometer shown here measured humidity. See the section on Measure for details.

"The Last Supper" was a painting of almost unrivaled fame from the moment when Leonardo finished it. Unfortunately, in this case the artist's scientific genius did not serve him well. As dampness seeped into the wall on which he painted the mural, it began to fade within a few years; for centuries it has been hardly visible. Had Leonardo used the ordinary fresco method, his work might be better preserved today.

"I WILL UNDERTAKE TO EXECUTE THE BRONZE HORSE," Leonardo wrote in a famous job-hunting letter to the Duke of Milan, "in the eternal memory of your father and of the very illustrious house of Sforza." He got the job, and he left Florence, continuing in Milan for many years, where he worked on the horse monument from time to time. He intended the statue to be 25 feet high, and it would have needed about 10 tons of bronze for casting. Leonardo actually completed the full-scale plaster model for the monument, and it stood in a public square at Milan, amazing all who saw it. Before he got around to casting it, though, the French invaded Milan, the Duke fled, and Leonardo departed. The artist had a lifelong interest in horses, and made a careful study of the horse's anatomy, comparing it with the structure of other animals and man.

MUSIC

"There can be no voice where there is no movement and trembling of the air; there can be no trembling of the air where there is no instrument."

In twentieth-century America, the air is full of music. Nearly every family has a radio to cause "movement and trembling of the air"; millions of phonograph records are bought each year, and concert groups visit all but the smallest towns. Like the people of every century before us, we need music for any sort of occasion, whether it's a school assembly or a dance at home, a church wedding or a parade. Yet in our novelty-seeking age, we usually turn to the past for our assembly songs, wedding marches, concert programs, and military music. Most of the concert music written by modern composers has little direct connection with the events of living, and relatively few people hear it. A composer generally gets an idea, writes it down, and hopes that his sonata, quartet, or symphony will be played.

A fifteenth-century composer wrote music because a particular occasion called for it and also because the music had been ordered by his patron. The composer might be writing for a church service, a court pageant, or a festival, but he always knew what the music was for when he began writing it, and he also knew it would be played. There were a few court concerts, where people gathered as they do now for the sole purpose of hearing music, but the equivalent of our concert music was also important as part of daily life.

We can only guess at how the music sounded, because the writing of notes did not then include directions about how fast or how loud a piece should be played, or exactly what instruments or how many should play it. We do know, though, that in Leonardo's time music, like the other arts, had loosened its ties with the church and found new uses for nonreligious celebrations. We know, too, that instruments were no longer limited to accompanying voices, but also had music of their own. While a modern orchestra consists mainly of strings, the wind instruments took first place in the fifteenth century. Modern double-reed instruments, for example, consist of the oboes and the bassoons, but there used to be ten families of instruments with double reeds where we now have two. Instruments were valued by collectors for their appearance as well as for their sound, so that they were often inlaid with ivory or rare wood and decorated by skillful painters.

When Leonardo came to Florence as a young man, he quickly won praise for his excellent lute playing. When he later left Florence for Milan, he supposedly took the trip partly to present a gift from Lorenzo de' Medici to Duke Ludovico Sforza; the gift was a silver lute shaped like a horsehead and made by Leonardo himself. Possibly, he did a little composing, though this is doubtful. But beyond his interest in music as an art, Leonardo studied the mechanics of musical instruments and tried to improve them. He devised plans to extend the usefulness of the trumpet, and he worked with the principle of the music box, applying it to instruments such as the drum.

Leonardo also wanted to know the nature of sound, and made experiments to find out about it. He placed dust on a board and showed how the dust would divide into little heaps when the board was beaten, thus demonstrating the vibrations of sound. This experiment might be compared to the much later demonstration of the way iron filings group themselves symmetrically on a piece of paper around the poles of a magnet under the paper.

Though he never guessed the almost incredible speed at which light travels, Leonardo realized that lightning and thunder happen at the same time, and that the lag between the lightning flash and the thunderclap means that light travels much faster than sound. He also realized that sound bounces off a surface in the same way that light bounces off a mirror. "Every blow struck against the object," he wrote, "bounds back at an angle equal to the angle of percussion"; this statement matches the familiar rule about light that the angle of reflection equals the angle at which light strikes a surface.

The sculptor, said Leonardo, creates his work by the strength of his arm; as he hammers away at the marble, "the marble dust flours him all over so that he looks like a baker," but the painter "sits before his work, perfectly at his ease and well dressed . . . and often he is accompanied by music or by the reading of various beautiful works which, since they are not mixed with the sound of the hammer or other noises, are heard with the greatest pleasure." It has been said that while Leonardo painted "Mona Lisa," he employed a group of musicians so that his model, Lisa Gherardini, would be amused and perfectly at her ease. As for this rather strange attack on sculptors, some people think he directed it against Michelangelo, whose super-human energy and passion were the very opposite of Leonardo's calm and detached approach to life. ✠

THIS TRUMPET WITH KEYS WAS TO PLAY A MORE COMPLETE SCALE than an ordinary trumpet. It appears at the left, extending into the margin, on this sketch of wind instruments. A trumpet that consists of a plain tube cannot play every note of the scale except in the very high register; nor can it shift from one musical key to another. Leonardo hoped to enlarge the trumpet's possibilities by adding keys: the player was supposed to press the keys between *ab* in the picture. (Leonardo's label is, as usual, written from right to left.) A supplementary upper tube carried wires from each key to devices opening and closing holes in the trumpet. Pressing the key pushed its wire, thereby opening one of the holes and changing the pitch. Such a trumpet might be six feet long or more. Since the player pushed the keys down with one hand and had only his other hand free to support the weight of the instrument, he put the loop at the mouthpiece end around his neck as an additional brace.

Leonardo's trumpet probably never passed the design stage. If it had, he would have discovered what was found out centuries later, when others tried a system much like his. Because of the shape of its tube, or bore, and the way it is played, a trumpet does not lend itself to a key system. The keys on modern trumpets actually form parts of valves; when the player presses a valve it opens a path to a little extra tubing, whereas keys merely open and shut holes.

The trumpet did not become a musical instrument until after 1600. In Leonardo's lifetime it was reserved for ceremonies and military use. Only noblemen had the privilege of keeping a trumpeter, and that is how the custom arose of hanging banners with coats of arms on trumpets.

The two lower instruments at the right of this picture seem to be variations of the key-trumpet idea, while the upper one is a simple type of organ with a handle to work what must be a bellows arrangement inside the box.

"A DRUM WITH COGS WORKING BY WHEELS WITH SPRINGS," as Leonardo described it, would be beaten automatically as the drum was wheeled along. The turning wheel axle sets in motion the two cage gears. You can see that the upper cylinders of these gears are studded with pegs, in the manner of a music-box cylinder. The placing of the pegs controls the rhythm of the drum, because they trip the spring-powered drumsticks. Five drumsticks on each side of the drum could produce quite an impressive noise for a snappy military parade. The drum that keeps the beat for a modern dance band hasn't as many drumsticks or complications as Leonardo's, but it can be played with the foot instead of the hand: pressure on a pedal causes the drumstick to beat.

The drum itself, of course, is one of the oldest of all instruments, and can be found in any type of civilization from the most primitive to the most complex. It didn't become a serious military instrument, though, until the time of the Crusades, when the Swiss thought of using it for the purpose. At about the same time, the fife entered military service too. The famous fife-and-drum corps of the American Revolution have a long tradition behind them.

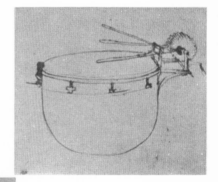

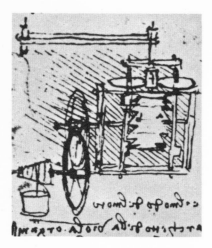

THIS BOW FOR A MECHANICAL VIOL was moved by clockwork. At the lower left, Leonardo has arranged a drum containing a spring. A cord connects the drum with a cone, called a fusee, directly above it. As the spring unwinds, the cord goes from the fusee to the drum, leaving the narrow end of the fusee first; the increasing circumference of the fusee offsets the decreasing power of the spring as it continues to unwind, and keeps the rate of motion even. Leonardo did not invent the fusee, but it was a new idea in his time. Until the spring and fusee were invented, clocks could not be carried from one place to another, as the weights used for power made them too heavy. Leonardo was undoubtedly one of the very first people to think of applying the fusee principle for another purpose.

The regulation of the viol bow appears to be managed by the wheel marked *ab*, similar to the escape wheel on a clock, except that the wheel has teeth on both edges of its rim. Leonardo specified in his note that the teeth on the two edges should not be level with each other, so that "the bow will have an even movement; otherwise it will go in jerks." The bow itself is pictured at the top. Before the days of the jukebox various restaurants used to have a machine in which an automatic violin played a repertory of tunes.

Leonardo called this instrument an organist viol. Apparently, he intended the bowing mechanism to be one part of a sort of one-man band, which also included a mechanical drum and an automatic keyboard instrument, but he didn't show the whole thing in one drawing.

THE BELL DOESN'T SWING, but remains stationary so that a hammer can strike one clear note at a time. The bell ringer pulls a rope as if he were ringing an ordinary bell; the rope moves a series of levers to pull the hammer away from the side of the bell, and a counterweight at the top and to the left of the bell acts as a spring to send the hammer against the bell when the rope is released.

The world's largest tuned bell, at Riverside Church, in New York City, has two hammers on opposite sides, one of which can be moved on the same principle as in Leonardo's bell, though the details differ. When a man pushes down a treadle, it sets in motion machinery using compressed air to push levers connected with the hammer. As the hammer weighs half a ton, and the bell weighs 20 tons, it would require too much exertion to ring the bell without the aid of power. The other hammer of this huge bell is moved by clockwork and strikes the hours, a custom that goes back many centuries. There is also a clapper inside the bell; to set it in motion, the bell is rocked back and forth by two motors that move wheels and drive chains on each side of the bell to start it swinging. When the swing reaches an arc of a certain length, the clapper swings back and forth too, ringing the bell.

The 20-ton bell at Riverside Church sounds the lowest note in the church's 74-bell carillon; the smaller bells work almost exactly the same way as Leonardo's, except that the levers connect with clappers inside the bells instead of hammers on the outside. All the bells in the carillon are rung by means of a large keyboard consisting of handles and treadles, so that the carillon player can ring several bells at a time for harmonic effects.

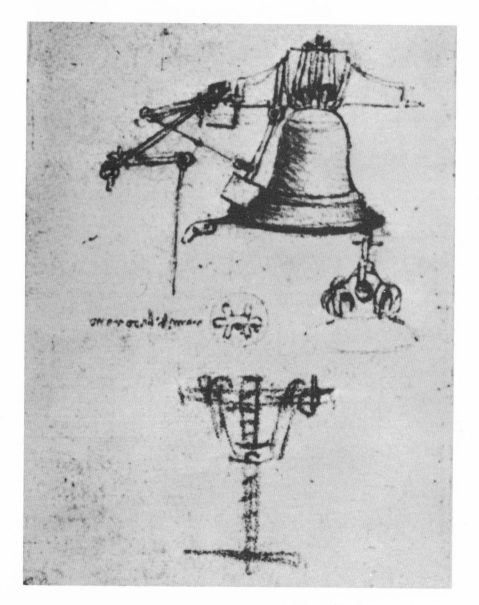

STAGE

"Books are filled with accounts of potent spells and spirits that speak without tongues or vocal organs, both of which are necessary for speech. The spirits speak, carry heavy weights, make storms and rain. Men turn into cats, wolves and other beasts. The first to turn into fools, however, are the writers who make such statements."

A theater audience comes prepared to lay aside the facts of the everyday world in favor of a new set of standards that create the reality of the stage. Time and distance can be magically spanned simply by dropping the curtain or dimming the lights between one scene and the next. A character may pass from youth to age in the space of two hours by altering his make-up and wearing a wig. Wars may be fought and won, kings may live and die, and miracles can happen. All these things become possible not only because magic is in the air but also because the production itself does much to create convincing illusions.

Styles of creating these stage illusions differ as much as fashions in dress. At one theater you may see Shakespeare's *Hamlet* performed with a conventional proscenium arch over the stage, realistic scenery, and elaborately costumed actors. The same play presented at another theater may dispense entirely with scenery, costumes, and curtain, and the audience may surround nearly the whole stage instead of facing one side of it. Which style brings the play to life most effectively is a matter of individual taste. In nineteenth-century American theaters, the trapdoor on the stage was so often used for burying Ophelia in the famous funeral scene of *Hamlet* that it came to be known as a Hamlet trap. Such a trapdoor offers one example of the machinery, often invisible, that makes so many stage situations believable. Because of turntables, lifting machinery, trapdoors, and pulleys, Peter Pan can fly, Don Giovanni can disappear into a flaming hell, and Lohengrin can ride away in a swan boat.

Stage machinery can be traced back to Greek and Roman times when the *deus ex machina*, the "god from the machine," descended from the sky by means of a crane to settle the problems of earthbound characters. Revolving scenery and rolling stages also go back to classical times. The revival of Greek and Roman ideas in the fifteenth century brought with it a revival of classical stage practices. Leonardo and his fellow artists who included stage design among their duties used machinery of all kinds. For a feeling of perspective, where we now use a backdrop to show a row of receding houses, the Renaissance designer called for the houses to be actually built in diminishing sizes so that the smaller houses in the background could give the illusion of distance. A rough sea could be produced by a series of parallel wavy cylinders strung across the stage; as men offstage turned the cranks at the ends of each cylinder, the cylinders revolved to give the effect of tossing waves. Likewise, the clouds in heaven were suspended from long poles held by men behind the scenes. Sound effects included firing a gun to make thunder, and colored lights were achieved in many ways, such as by placing a torch and a reflector behind a bottle of red or white wine.

Leonardo had no use for the medieval belief in magic, the practice of alchemy, and the superstition still prevalent in his time, but he enjoyed creating the magic of the stage. As a court artist, he not only designed scenery and costumes for many pageants, festivals, and masquerades, but he probably told stories and sang for the court as well. Not many of Leonardo's stage designs still survive, but the few existing sketches show that for one court pageant he thought of a two-piece revolving stage, so constructed that a mountain could be opened and closed, and for another he made use of a hoisting device to raise one of the characters to heaven. Since many of the pageants combined Christian and classical ideas, scenes in heaven were popular; the great architect Filippo Brunelleschi, who designed the dome for the cathedral of Florence, created one such scene by suspending from a cupola a circular framework that held a "bouquet of angels," actually a group of children. The framework revolved, and around it twinkling lights and bits of cotton wool became stars and fleecy clouds.

Early in life, the story goes, Leonardo was asked by his father to decorate a shield for a neighboring peasant. He supposedly filled his room with "lizards, hedgehogs, newts, serpents, dragonflies, locusts, bats, glowworms" and other beasts, and painted a "fearsome monster, hideous and appalling, breathing poison and flames," apparently a composite of all these unlovely creatures. In later years, the artist's taste in fantasy took a more genial turn: to introduce himself to the French King, Francis I, he devised a mechanical lion "which advanced a few steps, then opened its breast which was entirely filled with lilies."

Alarming or amusing, the world of make-believe appealed to Leonardo from first to last. ✠

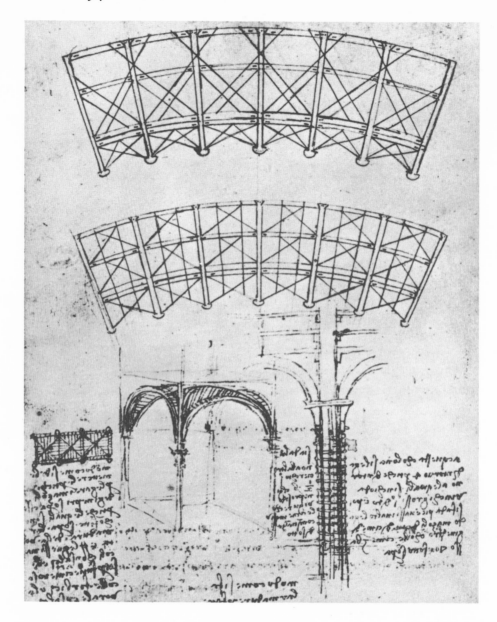

DECORATIVE SCAFFOLDING FOR A FESTIVAL was designed to be covered with bunches of juniper. If you followed Leonardo's advice about building the scaffold and arranging the juniper on it, the juniper would seem to be growing from the poles of the scaffold. The type of construction shown here still applies to the building of scenery and other temporary structures.

When the Medici became rulers of Florence, early in the fifteenth century, they introduced the idea of having public festivals to celebrate important events. The first one, held in 1418, featured a race of unbridled horses through a street of Florence still known as the Corso, meaning "race track," in honor of the event. Later, while

Leonardo was at work in Verrocchio's studio, Verrocchio supervised the arrangements for the great festival celebrating the betrothal of Lorenzo the Magnificent, the most remarkable of the Medici rulers. Leonardo himself may have made some of the elaborate helmets worn by people marching in the triumphal parade; even the horses were masked to look like lions or leopards, while the women dressed as Greek goddesses. This festival and the others like it would have called for dressing up the buildings as well as the people, and scaffolding covered with greenery was probably used.

Leonardo built a scaffold of a different sort for his own use when painting a mural in an important Florentine building. The scaffold was such that "it could be made higher by drawing it together, or lowered by making it wider," as an early biographer of Leonardo described it. The base may have been composed of a series of strips crossed like Xs and joined in such a way that the whole framework could be elongated or squeezed together; some adjustable lamp bases are made on this plan.

"TO MAKE A BEAUTIFUL COSTUME," says one of Leonardo's notes, "take fine cloth and give it a strong-smelling coat of varnish . . . and glaze it with scarlet kermes [a kind of dye], having the stencil perforated and moistened to prevent it from sticking. And let this stencil have a pattern of knots, which should afterwards be filled in with black millet, and the background with white millet." Leonardo enjoyed making intricate designs of knots as a decorative pattern, so it's easy to see why he recommended the idea to others.

He also enjoyed designing scenery and costumes, because stage design gave him a chance to be as fanciful as he pleased. The costumes shown here were probably sketched for the Paradise pageant given at the court of the Duke of Milan (see description of revolving stage for more details). Beautiful as they must have been, the elegant fashions of the court would have matched them in splendor. For a festive occasion, the courtiers dressed in brilliant brocades, often adorned with precious stones; the ladies' gowns might have long trains, and men wore colorful plumed hats. Ambassadors from nearby cities and faraway countries arrived on horseback, and the hall where they assembled was so grand that they could ride their horses through its very door. Before the pageant, there were ballets and round dances, and finally the heralds sounded a fanfare on their long trumpets to announce that the stage curtains would soon open.

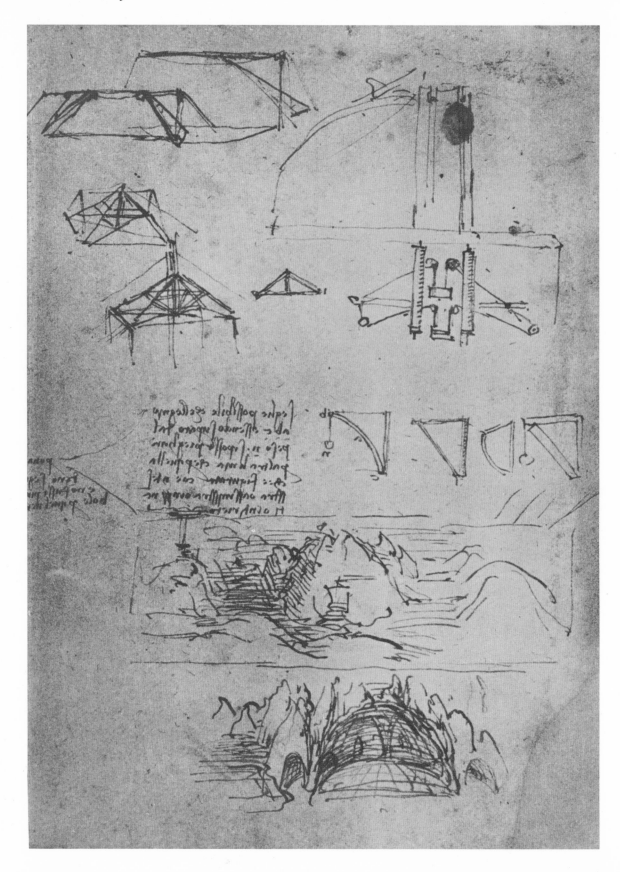

THIS SCENERY MOUNTAIN OPENED to give the audience a dazzling view of an egg-shaped Paradise with a gold-ceilinged dome, colored lights, and beautifully costumed actors representing the seven planets, to the accompaniment of sweet music. A man who saw the Paradise pageant, performed on January 10, 1490, for the court of Duke Ludovico Sforza in Milan, said of it, "And so great was the splendor of this marvelous decoration that one first believed they were seeing the real Paradise."

To make the mountain open and close, Leonardo built it in halves on two platforms with wheels that could roll over the main floor of the stage. Each half, shaped like a quarter of a pie, pivoted at stage center when a man under the stage worked a winch. The winch moved a lever-and-pulley system that connected with axles concealed in decorative pillars at each side of the stage.

The concept of revolving scenery goes back at least to Roman times. Leonardo may have seen the comment by Vitruvius, the Roman authority on architecture and theatrical matters, who referred to "triangular pieces of machinery which revolve, each having three decorated faces. When the play is to be changed," he said, "or when gods enter to the accompaniment of sudden claps of thunder, these may be revolved and present a face differently decorated."

In Leonardo's time, changes of scene were arranged more for surprise than for change of place. One writer on the subject even advised how to make surprises more effective. Have somebody in the audience start a fight, he suggested, and by the time people begin looking at the stage again the scene will be changed!

 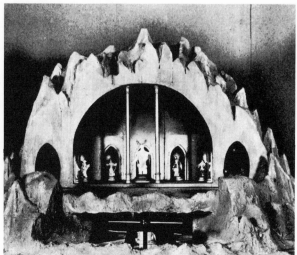

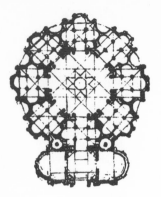

ARCHITECTURE

"A building ought always to be detached all around in order that its true shape can be seen."

In architecture, it is well known that "form follows function"; it is equally true that architecture mirrors the spirit of its age. The Parthenon, a temple to the Greek goddess of wisdom, symbolizes the Greek search for perfect harmony. The Gothic houses of worship took a very different form, reaching for heaven as did the people who built and prayed in them. Now churches no longer soar over the city landscape; it is the skyscraper, house of business, that towers over modern life. And the very towering of the skyscraper reveals our mastery of materials and building methods (see section on Construction for details).

The architect thus sums up both the temper and the technology of his times, designing houses that strive to carry out their function and achieve a form pleasing to the eye. He must understand both how to keep the roof from leaking and how to make it the crowning glory of his building. Unlike the taste of most periods, the modern view of architectural beauty makes few demands for ornament: where the designers of Greek temples or Renaissance palaces allowed for colonnades, statues, and decoration, our skyscraper designers allow for electric wires, telephone lines, plumbing pipes, and elevators. The handmade buildings of the past, with their individual touches of genius, have for the most part given place to buildings that typify the machine age in their soundness of structure, convenience of use, and sameness of looks.

When Leonardo was painting "The Last Supper" in the Milanese church of Santa Maria delle Grazie, his friend Donato Bramante, a leading Renaissance architect, was putting the dome on the same church. About 50 years earlier, Filippo Brunelleschi had completed the huge dome for the cathedral of Florence. The first architect of the Italian Renaissance, he took as his model not the tall pointed arches and spires of the Gothic cathedral but the symmetry of a Roman temple such as the Pantheon, round and massive. Brunelleschi's dome, still the memorable landmark of Florence, was so large that it could have cast a shadow over the city's entire population; it marked the beginning of a time when architecture would be guided by classic standards of beauty rather than by the symbolism that inspired the cathedrals; it was also the first important structure to be designed by an individual architect who had won a competition in order to get the job.

Though he knew well how to build a huge church or an ordinary house, Leonardo seems to have dealt more with the theory than with the practice of architecture. He was deeply interested in geometric forms, and took advantage of the new popularity of the dome and of the circular shape in his many designs for churches. He carried the idea of a round building even to fortress design, thus taking a leap into the future (see section on War for details).

Leonardo did not confine his attention to large public buildings, however, but thought about private houses, large and small, and how they should be built to meet the practical problems of living. Writing about the way a certain palace should be planned, he noted: "The rooms which you mean to use for dancing . . . should be on the ground floor, for I have seen them collapse. . . . Let the mezzanines of the dwellings be divided by walls made of narrow bricks, and without beams because of the risk of fire. . . . All the privies should have ventilation openings . . . ," and so on. His designs for multiple flights of stairs were also for convenience, and the comfort of horses occupied Leonardo's attention too; he devised a plan to keep a stable clean and to make the horses' food easily available.

And he applied his concern for practical living to the design of whole cities as well as that of the individual house. Leonardo worked at a time when every architect enjoyed drawing plans for the ideal city. While others worked on inventing unusual geometric shapes for their city outlines, Leonardo began with health and convenience as his guiding principles. The city wall, constructed for military reasons, meant little to him: he preferred an open city with wide streets and many canals. Sewage disposal, not a subject of wide interest at the time, figured prominently in his plans, and so did decentralization. For reasons of health he suggested distributing the population of Milan into smaller units, "and you will disperse so great a concourse of people, who, herding together like goats . . . sow the seeds of pestilence and death."

Even the idea of houses built with prefabricated parts occurred to Leonardo: "The houses are first made in parts upon the open places, and are then fitted together with their timbers on the spot where they are to remain." ✠

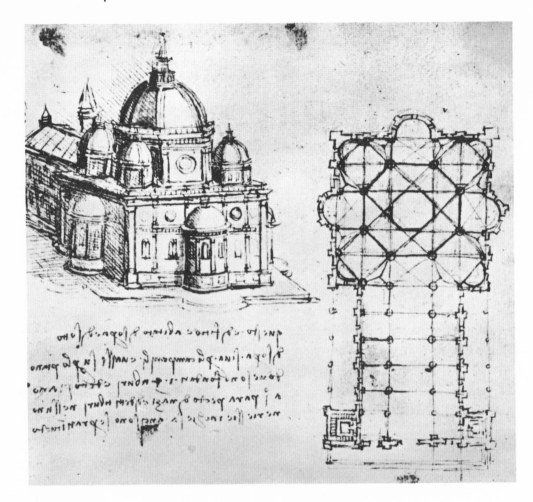

COMBINATIONS OF CIRCLE AND SQUARE interested Leonardo as ideas for drawing church plans, partly because he enjoyed making geometric designs, his form of doodling. But there was also a good architectural reason. In Leonardo's time the dome became very popular as the focal point of church buildings. The great domed church of St. Peter's in Rome, for example, originally had a square ground plan. St. Peter's was designed by Bramante, a master architect of the Renaissance and a friend of Leonardo's. Some years after Bramante died, Michelangelo continued building the church, designed its dome, and lived, at age eighty-nine, to see half the dome completed. A square, with its four equal sides, makes a suitable base for a dome, setting it off well; Leonardo understood this point.

As court engineer, Leonardo sometimes made suggestions about church construction, but designs like the one in this picture were not done with any particular building project in mind.

Always practical, Leonardo based some of his church plans on achieving the best acoustic effects. One of these, which he called a "theater for preaching," had both Roman and twentieth-century features. From the outside, this church looked like a large ball with the top and bottom cut off. Tiers of arches and flights of steps covered the outside in the Roman manner; inside, rows of seats lined the bulging wall. But the startling thing about this church was its ground plan, which resembled two-thirds of a circle. A column, supporting the pulpit at the top, stood at the circle's center. To have thought of the ear as well as the eye in church design puts Leonardo far ahead of his time.

LEONARDO'S CITY SHAPED LIKE A SPINDLE had a decentralized design, with special districts for craftsmen, such as textile workers, and for merchants. The shaded strip around the edge is probably a canal rather than a wall. Canals, Leonardo believed, would serve the double purpose of keeping the air pure and supplying an extra means of transportation.

City planning goes back at least as far as Babylon, where Queen Semiramis had her famous hanging gardens, one of the seven wonders of the ancient world. The ancient peoples, especially the Romans, tended to plan for the purposes of health and convenience, just as Leonardo did. But by his day, ideas had changed and city planners were more interested in power and glory for the city's rulers.

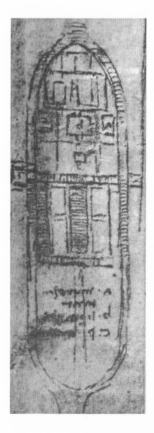

In America, William Penn was probably the first city planner. Like Leonardo, Penn chose a river site for his city; unlike Leonardo's plans, however, Penn's were carried through. He laid out Philadelphia in the large gridiron that has become standard in many American cities, and he directed that each house be surrounded by a garden, fields, and orchards. This layout would give the city the pleasant green and good air of the countryside. Penn's city was built in huge square plots; around 1684, when Penn left to return to England, Philadelphia must have been a true garden spot. By the time he made a second visit to America, in 1699, the plots had already been divided and subdivided because the city had grown so fast. In only fifteen years the garden spot had developed slums!

Leonardo devised several of his city plans after the disastrous plague of 1485 killed one out of every six people in Milan, fifty thousand victims all told. Because there was no known cure for the plague once it got started, he believed the only thing to do was to spread people out and try to avoid infection by means of clean air and good sanitation, a completely modern point of view.

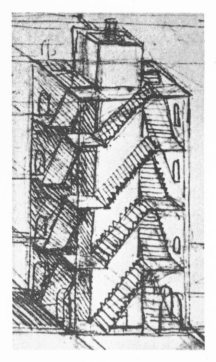

SEPARATE FLIGHTS OF STAIRS to reach different parts of a building avoided a traffic jam on the staircase. Like a modern escalator system, these flights could be divided, one for going up and another for going down, or they could be used for privacy in entering or leaving one's own apartment. Leonardo's multiple-stairway designs included one for two flights that started from opposite corners on one side of the building and passed each other at the halfway point, resembling a large X on one wall. The idea of building stairs on the outside of a house has been used occasionally in European architecture, but is seen most often in the modern fire escape. Leonardo also drew a double spiral staircase for two-way traffic; such a staircase exists in the Statue of Liberty.

THIS DOUBLE-DECKER CITY WAS DESIGNED FOR HEALTH and comfort. Its roads on two levels served different purposes, as Leonardo explained: "No vehicles should go in the upper roads [which he intended to run 12 feet above the lower level]; these should be reserved for the use of gentlemen. And on the lower roads would go the carts and barrows and things used by the populace." The roads were to be as wide as the height of the houses, a modern idea, and a third level of passages for sewage ran underground. Street openings at fixed intervals on the lower roads, like the gratings at our street corners, let rain and sewage drain through. At every arch, Leonardo specified, there should be a spiral staircase leading from upper to lower level: "At the first turn [of each staircase] should be a door of entry into the privies. . . . Let such a city be built near the sea, or some large river, so that the impurities of the city may be carried far away by water."

In its whole concept, this plan is up to date; divided traffic and sanitation rank as two prime concerns in modern city plans. Four hundred years after Leonardo drew this sketch, Charles Wacker worked out a plan for a section of downtown Chicago with precisely the same ideas in mind. For the sake of health, he wanted to provide plenty of open space and parks. To speed traffic, he proposed two-level roads very similar to Leonardo's: the upper level served stores and private traffic, while the streets below passed the basements of buildings fronting them and were meant for deliveries and trucking. Furthermore, he too envisaged a third underground level, not for sewage but for a subway that would make it easy for people to reach the area from other parts of the city.

Mr. Wacker's plan was carried out in a limited way. Chicago's Wacker Drive, named for him, is a two-level street more than a mile long. Private cars run on both levels, but buses travel on the top street only, and trucks mainly on the bottom. Its length includes a two-level bridge across the Chicago River; the bridge can be raised in the middle from each end to permit boats to pass through. The subway finally got built, too. A man of vision, Wacker missed his guess on only one point. Writing in 1902, he predicted that in fifty years' time Chicago would be the world's largest city with a population of 13,500,000.

CONSTRUCTION

"You know that medicines when well used restore health to the sick, and he who knows them well will use them well when he also knows what man is, and what life and the constitution are, and what health is. . . . In just the same way a cathedral in need of repair requires a doctor-architect who understands well what a building is. . . ."

For the Chicago Century of Progress fair of 1933, Frank Lloyd Wright suggested a 250-story skyscraper, half a mile tall, which would house all the exhibits and truly reflect the progress in construction during the previous hundred years. He wrote that "such construction today would be no impossible feat, financially or structurally." Twenty-three years later, in 1956, Mr. Wright had doubled the size of building he believed possible, and designed a mile-high skyscraper, also for construction in Chicago. This building was to have 528 stories of ten feet each, floors that projected like balconies from a central concrete core, tapering as it rose; an outside surface of gold metal and glass, and elevators that looked like railroad cars set on end and could let off passengers at five floors at a time.

Though neither of Wright's skyscrapers has been erected, the fact that such an important architect thought them practical shows how dramatically building materials and construction methods have changed in the recent past. The revolution in building began only in the 1880's, with the introduction of the steel-girder frame for supporting weight; before then, skyscrapers in the modern sense would not have been possible. Gothic cathedrals, the skyscrapers of the Middle Ages, were supported by their own outer walls, reinforced by buttresses; only a cathedral could justify the immense quantity of materials and labor needed for this method of skyscraper-building. Now we have both steel and reinforced concrete to make strong and economical frames, and panels of glass and metal for the outer walls. A Renaissance builder walking down one of our newer business streets would hardly recognize the building materials and would probably wonder what prevents the buildings from falling to the ground.

Today, we have pretested materials and mathematical tables to tell us how much weight a beam or column can safely support, but the fifteenth-century builder had only his experience to guide him. He managed to pile stone on stone to support his great churches and palaces without our new methods and also without our theoretical knowledge of construction. It was in the area of theory that Leonardo shone: nobody before him had thought of finding out on paper, as it were, how to establish margins of safety for building. He considered the problems just as we do now, working in terms of the strength of materials when loaded with weight, and judging what proportions of a column or beam would be the strongest. In order to make scientific investigations, Leonardo would compare columns of the same thickness but different length, or of the same length but different thickness. By varying only one dimension at a time, he could make his tests theoretically useful.

For example, he wrote, "Of all supports of similar material and equal thickness, the shorter one will sustain more weight than the longer one by as much as it is shorter than the longer one." Such a statement may not seem unusual now, but Leonardo was the first person ever to approach construction this way.

His studies of supporting weight were matched by his studies of lifting weight: he tried to discover the most effective designs for lever and pulley systems by investigating the theory behind their use. Thus he was able to design lifting machines, such as cranes and jacks, that offered great mechanical advantage; that is, they lifted the maximum weight for a given expenditure of manpower.

Leonardo examined the reasons why an arch supports weight, calling it a "strength built of two weaknesses," and he thought about why cracks develop in walls and how to deal with them. He reminded himself to "make first a treatise of the causes which bring about the collapse of walls, and then, separately, a treatise of the remedies."

The Duke of Milan and others often consulted Leonardo about structural problems, especially those of the Milan cathedral, and they may have taken some of his advice. But when he suggested lifting a church in Florence so as to add a flight of steps to its approach, people thought him foolish. The fact is that Leonardo could have supervised such an operation with success.

Despite the difference in the knowledge and building materials of their times, Frank Lloyd Wright in the twentieth century and Leonardo in the fifteenth had one thing in common: both believed that a building, like a person, must have integrity, and achieve its outer beauty from inner strength and soundness. ✤

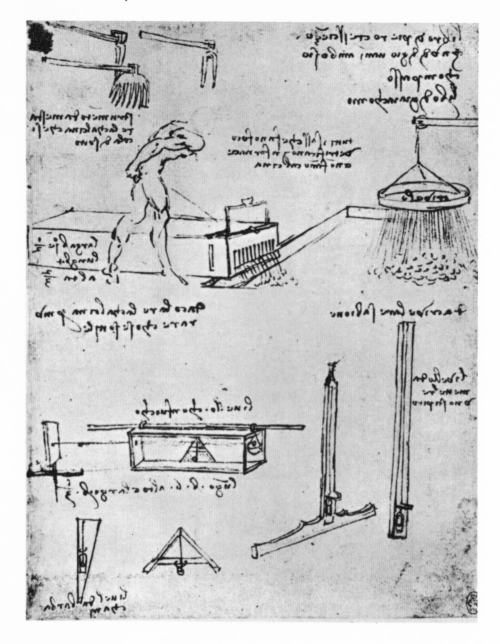

"MORTAR FOR THIN WALLS," Leonardo reports, is made by the method shown in this sketch. The forklike tools at the top are meant for stirring a mixture of lime and water in the flat box guarded by the headless figure lower on the page. Lime, made by burning limestone, comes out of the furnace in the form of quicklime, and becomes slaked lime after it has been mixed with water. Mixing quicklime with water produces a strong chemical reaction: the mixture sizzles and sends off a great quantity of heat. In Leonardo's sketch, the liquid mixture drains through the slots at the end of the box into a larger tank, where sand is sifted into it from the strainer suspended over the tank. Mortar made by mixing slaked lime and sand has been in use since Roman times, and continues to be used in brick and stone construction. The modern mixture for mortar also contains Portland cement to make it harden faster. Not too long ago, mortar was still being mixed on the job, by a method very similar to the one Leonardo has sketched.

At the bottom of his page, Leonardo shows an assortment of levels for construction jobs. All of them depend on the plumbline; the spirit level, such as carpenters use today, wasn't invented until the seventeenth century. The spirit level, which you read by noting the position of an air bubble in a sealed vial of liquid, gets its name because the liquid used is alcohol. And alcohol is used because it won't freeze in cold weather.

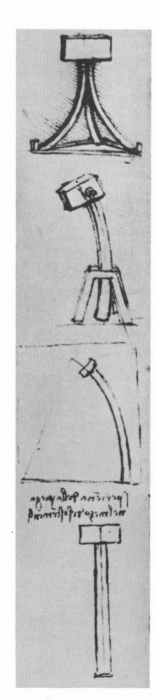

Among the levels shown here, the long box with a hole at each end is the most interesting. To use it for a purpose such as laying a level floor, you set up the box at one end of the area to be floored, placing it so that its two holes make a line pointing to the other end. Then you carry the spiked square board, at the left, to the far end of the area. You look through the hole in the board, raising and lowering the board until you have lined up this hole with the two holes in the box. At that height, the horizontal strip below the board will be exactly even with the bottom of the box. Because the board's spike sticks in the ground, you can leave the board there as a guide. The modern instrument called a transit works on the same principle, using a lens instead of sighting-holes.

These pictures seem to be a record of the tools and instruments in use at the time rather than inventions of Leonardo's.

How do wooden columns bend when loaded with too much weight? Questions like this one interested Leonardo because the answers served as guides to safe building construction. In the drawing at the top of this sketch, he shows that an excessive weight placed on top of three equal columns arranged as a tripod will bend them in the middle, "and the reason is that the pressure of the weight on top goes down through the whole support, and reaches the base as well as the top." The midpoints, farthest from both ends of the beams, are weakest and therefore bend first. When you break a stick over your knee, pulling it down at both ends, you are doing what Leonardo illustrates here: putting pressure on the middle of the stick, the weakest point in its length, to break it more easily.

"A vertical support that is not exactly centered under the weight on top will lean toward the side of the largest part of the weight," Leonardo noted next to the second drawing. But the drawing at the bottom shows that "it is impossible that the vertical support with its center directly under the center of the weight can ever bend; it would first be pushed into the ground."

Other studies he made along these lines described the relative strength of short and tall columns of a given width, and the advantages of making a support by binding together many thin rods, rather than using one thick rod. Leonardo also dealt with the problem of placing heavy weights on horizontal beams. While modern engineers can follow proven rules for safety margins in construction, no formulas to guide them could be worked out until studies like Leonardo's were done. His work actually came several hundred years before the theoretical rules were established; in his time, safety was a matter of trial and error. Even now, costly construction errors can occur. When a large new exhibit hall was being built in New York City not too long ago, the concrete floor collapsed and had to be begun all over again.

"TO FIND THE LOAD AN IRON WIRE CAN CARRY," Leonardo wrote, "attach an iron wire two braccia [about four feet] long to something that will properly support it. Then attach a basket or any similar container to the wire and pour into the basket some fine sand through a small hole placed at the end of the hopper. A spring is fixed so that it will close the hole as soon as the wire breaks. The basket is not upset while falling because it falls through a very short distance. The weight of the sand and the location of the break in the wire are to be noted. The test is repeated several times to check the results."

Measuring the strength of a wire was a new idea at the time; now it is an essential step in steel-wire manufacture. Instead of a basket filled with sand, the modern system makes use of hydraulic pressure and a dial indicating the amount applied, but the problem and the purpose of the test have not changed. Steel wire for our suspension-bridge cables can carry an astonishing amount of weight: one wire about as wide as a pencil can sustain a suspended weight of at least three tons before it breaks. Each of the four main cables of the new Verrazano-Narrows Bridge across New York harbor contains over 26,000 of these wires; they will support the 51,000-ton bridge and the weight of the traffic crossing it. A little multiplication will show you that there is a wide margin of safety. All this wire adds up to 145,000 miles.

Lacking accurate measurement tools, Leonardo used the weight of falling sand to measure the stress required to break the iron wire. A hundred years later, Galileo still faced the same difficulty, and used the weight of falling water as a standard of measurement. Galileo was experimenting with the time it took a ball to roll down an inclined plane; he wanted to measure the time so accurately, he said, that the difference between one test and another would never exceed "one-tenth of a pulse beat." Like Leonardo, Galileo repeated his test several times to check the results.

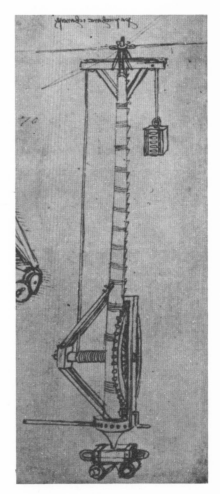

AN OVERHEAD WIRE GUIDES THIS MOVABLE CRANE so that it can travel back and forth in front of a house being built and hoist stone blocks at whatever point they are needed. A sort of double-acting connection between the crane and the wire permits the crane to revolve as well as to move forward while keeping its hold on the wire. Leonardo mounted the crane by means of a pivot on the base to make revolving it easy. To lift the stone blocks, a man works the handle at the bottom of the crane, on the right, which turns a very small gear meshed with a very large one. Moving at a much slower rate than the small gear, the large gear exerts correspondingly more power.

Leonardo's use of gears makes weight-lifting much less laborious than the Greek and Roman system, which depended on pulleys and a winch. For heavy loads, as many as five men might walk inside a treadmill like a huge squirrel cage; the cage served as the winch, winding the rope around a shaft as it turned and thus lifting the weight. It seems strange that the Romans failed to take advantage of gears for lifting, as they used gears for other purposes; but what looks obvious in one century is sometimes completely out of range in another. Part of Leonardo's mechanical genius lay in the fact that he could see new uses for existing labor-saving devices, and thereby brought a new approach to machine design. Gears or no gears, however, Archimedes managed to astonish everyone by towing a fully loaded ship over dry land; he did it with a complicated pulley system. It was the achievement of this unheard-of feat that supposedly caused him to make the memorable comment, "Give me a place to stand, and I will move the world."

Modern chain hoists make use of gears in much the same way as Leonardo's crane except, of course, for the source of power. Movable cranes now travel on tracks rather than under guide wires; they are generally used at a fixed place like a dock, where they load ships, or a power station, where they move coal. To lift a medium-heavy load such as a railroad engine, a crane may have a series of gears that get successively larger in order to step up the power more effectively. The heaviest loads of all, like the sluice gates for a huge dam, may weigh hundreds of tons and are hoisted by a different method: a hydraulic lift does the job.

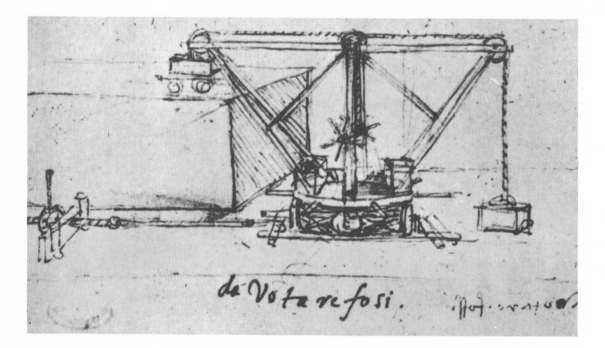

BLOCKS OF STONE ARE PASSENGERS on this double crane that has a counterweight feature similar to that of a modern elevator's. Leonardo designed it to simplify removal of stone blocks as they were cut from the huge slab at the left. While men on top of the slab load a block into one crane, men on the ground unload another block already brought down by the other crane; when the empty crane is hoisted by turning the spoked wheels on the crane mast, the loaded crane automatically descends, thus providing a heavy counterweight that makes the lifting job much easier. The crane rests on a turntable that can be readily revolved by pushing the handles projecting from it, and to the far left is a winch to pull the whole crane along as workmen continue cutting more blocks from the great stone slab.

To have a modern elevator with two cars balancing each other this way would not be convenient, because one car would have to go down at just the same time as the other went up, making all the same stops. But an elevator car has a heavy counterweight connected to it by a pulley system, and in principle works like Leonardo's cranes. When the car is empty, it exactly balances the counterweight; when the car is loaded with passengers, the counterweight moving in the opposite direction makes the car easier to raise or lower. We save electricity by arranging elevators with counterweights, while Leonardo saved manpower with his crane. Modern cranes, however, do not generally have counterweights, because they would interfere with the flexibility of the crane. Many cranes have their own power source, usually a Diesel engine that forms part of the machinery and travels on it. The T-shaped hammerhead crane, which most closely resembles Leonardo's double-crane design, can lift a load of 200 tons. But some jobs traditionally done by cranes are now being dealt with another way: Leonardo, who thought of using air as a source of power, would have enjoyed the idea of loading grain into a ship by the modern method of blowing it into the holds.

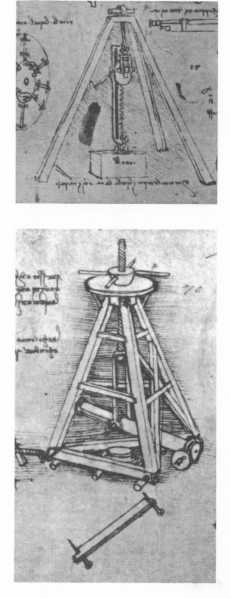

To LIFT HEAVY WEIGHTS in construction jobs, Leonardo designed a ratchet jack. It hung inside a huge tripod, with the hook down, and could raise a stone weighing half a ton. He also drew another kind of lifting jack worked by a screw in place of a ratchet. Both these types of jack had probably been in use for some time before Leonardo drew them; the screw jack, at least, had been sketched two hundred years earlier. Fifteenth-century soldiers used the ratchet jack to pull back the heavy strings of their large crossbows. The jack rested on the bow's mounting and, instead of the usual lifting hook on the end, it had two claws to grip the string.

A ratchet jack can be adjusted to a desired position faster than a screw jack, but the screw jack is easier to use because its motion is continuous. The garage jacks that lift a whole car in a few seconds use hydraulic power, the pressure of liquid, to raise a ram under the car. The liquid can be quickly released through a valve to lower the car again.

It can be seen immediately that Leonardo's ratchet looks like an automobile jack turned upside down. To change a tire, we lift the car from below rather than pulling it up from above, but the principle remains exactly the same.

FLIGHT

"See how the wings striking against the air hold up the heavy eagle in the thin upper air, near to the element of fire. And likewise see how the air moving over the sea strikes against the bellying sails, making the loaded heavy ship run; so that by these demonstrative and definite reasons you may know that man with his great contrived wings, battling the resistant air and conquering it, can subject it and rise above it."

The most important flight ever made in a power-driven airplane lasted 12 seconds and covered a distance of 120 feet. We all know that the flyer was Orville Wright, who had developed the plane he called the *Flyer* with his brother Wilbur, and that the year was 1903. The Wrights were not dreamers: they brought about a new age by systematic study of their subject and a series of carefully planned tests with gliders. Their practical thinking was matched by an ability to carry out their thoughts; when they could not persuade any existing company to build them a light, powerful airplane motor, they built it themselves. And their feat of flying in a machine heavier than air was so amazing that several years went by before many people really believed they had done it.

Aviation has advanced so rapidly that now we already have a plane capable of flying at 2,000 miles an hour, and the old dream of traveling to the moon, and possibly to other planets, promises to come true. But if the Wrights had to build their own motor for flight in a heavy airplane to become possible in 1903, flight in the fifteenth century was completely out of the question. Flying depends on moving weight fast enough so that its speed can overcome the forces of air resistance, which retards a plane, and gravity, which pulls it down. Until a lightweight motor was developed to accomplish the necessary speed, mankind had to remain earthbound except for gliding, or rising in a lighter-than-air balloon.

Many people have attempted to explain why Leonardo devoted so much of his energy to trying to make a flying machine and why he insisted on pursuing an approach that his own knowledge proved to be wrong. "Remember that your bird should have no other model than the bat," he wrote, because he understood that this flying mammal swoops like a glider and that its wing permits no air to pass through, as if it were a "bellying sail." But after giving himself this piece of excellent advice, Leonardo ignored it and spent years on the futile project of inventing a machine that would imitate the flapping flight of feathered birds. As he developed his machines, he kept adding more devices to give the pilot more comfort and better control. One machine had wing slots resembling the slots on a modern airplane wing that the flyer raises or lowers to change his altitude or brake his speed; one had a tail quite similar in design to the modern tail for steering; some included landing gear; and several had winches and pulley systems to make better use of the flyer's muscle power. One sketch even showed a spring system that served as an extra means of giving the machine lift. However, each new device simply added weight to the machine, thus making it more and more difficult to raise from the ground, because there was no adequate source of power.

If Leonardo had worked on inventing a glider, he might have been the first person to fly. As it was, he earned the honor of being the first person to study flight in a scientific manner. He spent countless hours observing the flight of birds through the air, noticing every detail of how they rose and descended, turned, swooped, and soared. He tried to duplicate their wing structure, which of course couldn't be done, but he found out much about the way birds use their wing bones and feathers. He also studied the currents of the air, and how the air interacts with a bird to keep it aloft, just as the water buoys up a swimmer. Leonardo made a few mistakes about bird flight, but he was right about many of its aspects and understood how the air must be used to make flight possible. Improving on his knowledge, we have now become masters of the air, but we still cannot build a machine that uses power as well as the bird in terms of its weight.

Like a modern flyer, Leonardo thought of safety as an important matter: "This machine," he said of one design, "should be tried over a lake, and you should carry a long wineskin as a girdle so that in case you fall you will not be drowned." And he thought of the parachute, but considered it a separate means of transportation rather than a safety device to be carried on a flying machine.

Most unexpected of all, Leonardo developed the idea of the modern helicopter. Taking his inspiration from a Chinese toy, he designed an aerial screw that was meant to be rapidly whirled for bearing people aloft. Again he lacked a good enough power source, but our present-day helicopters carry out his theory. The airport of Rome, named for Leonardo, displays a statue of him holding a model of his aerial screw for all to see. ✠

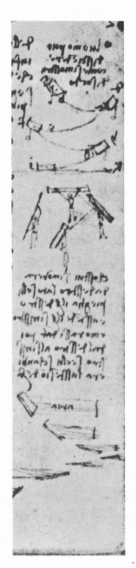

FALLING LEAVES SUGGESTED GLIDER FLIGHT to Leonardo, who pictured both ideas in one sketch. He also wrote a note to himself: "Make tomorrow, out of various shapes of cardboard, figures descending through the air, falling from our jetty; and then draw the figures and the movements made by the descent of each, in various parts of its descent." Apparently, he never carried the notion any further, but the sketch and the note prove that he conceived of gliding long before anyone else did.

The kite, invented by the Chinese, is a glider and the oldest man-made device that flies. It served the English baronet Sir George Cayley as a model when, in 1804, he built a five-foot glider that looked like a kite with a pole down the middle. Four years later, Sir George built another such glider that actually flew, though without a passenger. And in 1852, still pursuing his flying-machine studies, he designed still another glider and sent his coachman aloft in it. Thus, as he glided across a small English valley near Sir George's country manor, the coachman became the first airplane passenger in history. A sketch of this glider shows one large kitelike wing under which hangs a wheeled gondola with a figurehead on its prow: appropriately, the figurehead is a bird. Cayley, whose researches in flight are now regarded as basic to all later studies, also invented the caterpillar tractor.

Half a century after the coachman took his historic flight, the Wright brothers were flying in their gliders at Kitty Hawk, North Carolina, making ready to launch the first power-driven airplane. If Leonardo had followed up his glider sketch, he might have had more success with his flying machines centuries earlier.

LIKE A MAN ON A SLED, the aviator lies flat, steering with his hands and flapping the wings by kicking his feet up and down in opposite directions; one foot lowers the wings and the other foot raises them by means of pulley connections. Leonardo designed several machines of this type, with poles of cane and taffeta wings. The machine relies on muscle power to raise the flyer from the ground and carry him through the sky. Even though Leonardo realized that a man lacks the concentrated muscle power to imitate a bird, he continued trying to figure out how it could be done.

Before we laugh at what seem to be obvious defects of this machine, however, we should consider that Leonardo was neither the first nor the last to think of people flying like birds. In England,

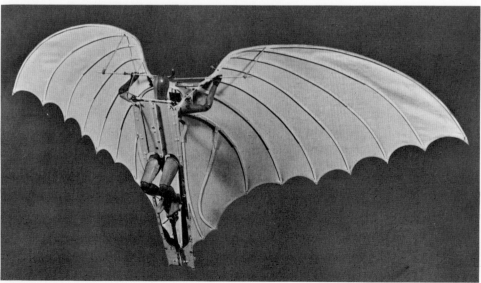

legend says that Bladud, father of King Lear, tried unsuccessfully, in 850 B.C. or thereabouts, to fly over London. In China, around the year 1500, a man named Wan Hoo attached large kites to his body and sent himself off by exploding many rockets, also attached. That was the end of Wan Hoo. An eighteenth-century drawing shows kites as a means of airlifting soldiers to their destination, and the idea of people flying with kites persisted into the nineteenth century. A kite, of course, resembles an airplane with fixed wings rather than the flapping wings of Leonardo's machines, but the kite-borne flyer resembles Leonardo's birdman in that he wears wings and makes use of air currents rather than riding in a high-powered machine.

The birdman is at last a reality, and he flies by a method similar to Wan Hoo's rocket power. The army has developed a system of flight by the release of compressed air: the soldier wears air tanks on his back as if he were a skindiver, and a gadget on his belt enables him to release the air in a powerful stream. Like a rocket, the man rises by the power of reaction. At the latest report, birdmen could fly a distance of about 600 feet at an altitude of 40 to 50 feet, but within a decade they may be able to travel 10 miles by this method. Meanwhile, the sporting British continue to pursue Leonardo's idea of muscle-powered flight. At *their* latest report, John Wimpenny of the Hatfield Man-Powered Aircraft Club pedaled madly to lift his machine, a sort of glider-bicycle, and propel it 990 feet through the air.

A RETRACTABLE LANDING GEAR for a flying machine is pictured opposite in two positions. The upper sketch illustrates how to stow it under the "fuselage," actually a plank, after the machine gets off the ground; below, Leonardo drew it extended to the ground for use in landing and boarding the machine. He explained his design: "These hooks that are underneath the feet of the ladder act in the same way as when one jumps on the points of one's toes, for then one is not stunned as is the person who jumps upon his heels . . . these ladders serve the same purpose as the legs and you can beat the wings while it is rising. . . . But when you have raised yourself, draw up the ladders as I show in the second figure above." To draw up the ladder as Leonardo directs, the flyer turns the winch above the plank.

This design typifies Leonardo's unrealistic approach to the problem of flight: he had the details straight but missed the main point. In nearly all his other studies, the insight of his mind and the keen observation of his eyes brought him very close to the truth, but in trying to discover how to fly, he seems to have been diverted from the truth by imagining himself to be a bird. You can see that he lands the machine on three supports placed like the wheels of a modern airplane and that they can be drawn up in the same way; in our airplanes, hydraulic power replaces Leonardo's winch for the purpose. If he could only have raised his machine into the air and kept it there at will, the landing gear would have served him well.

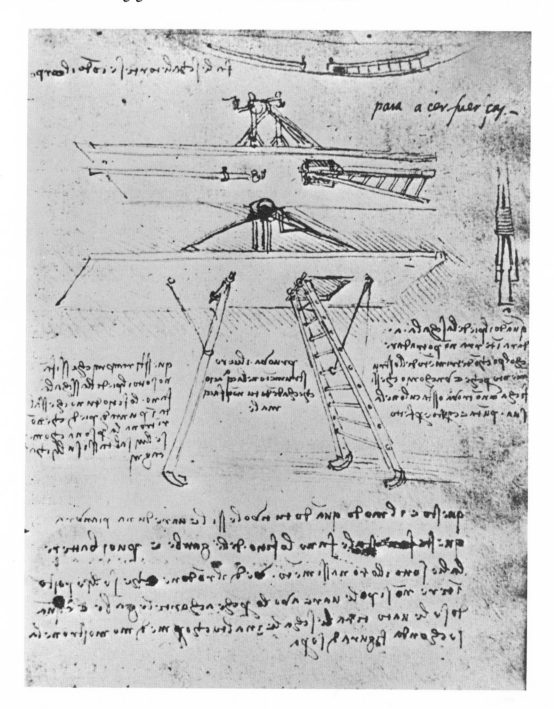

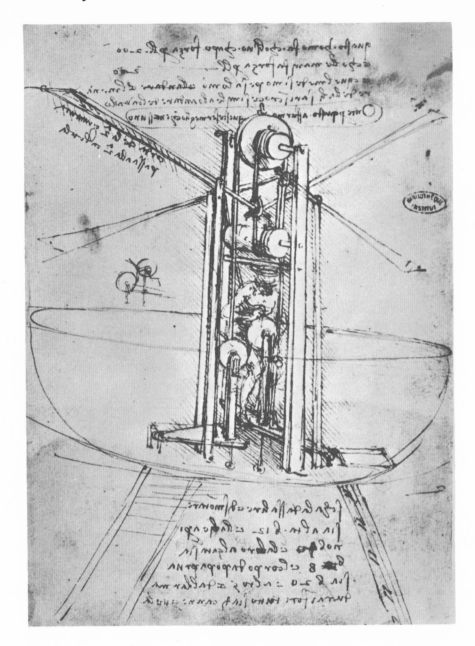

THIS FLYING SAUCER HAD OARLIKE WINGS that moved "crosswise after the manner of the gait of the horse," as Leonardo described it. The flyer moved them by turning a winch with his hands and exerting leverage with his head. Leonardo appears to have been carried away here by his new plan to have the flyer stand instead of lying flat. You can see at a glance that the whole idea of the machine will never work.

The airplane belongs to our times, but we cannot claim the invention of the flying saucers that have mystified so many people in recent years. In 1561, the good folk of Nuremberg rose to greet the sunrise one morning only to be alarmed by the sight of many large globes in the sky, some of them blood red and others blue-black. Then, as now, flying saucers were apparently contagious: a few years later, they turned up again in Basel. A news sheet illustrated the event with a woodcut of these ominous objects, and reported them as "moving before the sun with great speed and turning against each other as if fighting." In keeping with modern streamlined design, the flying saucer has changed its shape from a globe to a cigar, and it glitters instead of being red or black. It has also been dignified with the name of Unidentified Flying Object, or UFO for short. Otherwise, it's as ominous, mysterious, and improbable as ever.

Leonardo's flying saucer isn't the real thing, because it won't fly and it lacks mystery. Yet in one respect it is remarkable. Leonardo has drawn here what is probably the first design in history for a flying machine with a mechanical aid to amplify muscle power.

TRAVEL BY PARACHUTE occurred to Leonardo. He wrote, "If a man have a tent of closely woven linen without any apertures, twelve braccia across and twelve in depth, he can throw himself down from any great height without injury." A braccio was an arm's length, or a little less than 2 feet, so the parachute would have been about 24 feet square and high. It is supposed to have been successfully tested from a tower, almost three hundred years before the first definitely known parachute jump was made in 1783 from an observatory tower in France, although dogs had been parachuted from balloons a few years earlier in the eighteenth century.

Leonardo thought of the parachute as a means of getting from a higher to a lower place, not as a safety device for use with a flying machine. For safety when flying, he suggested wearing a string of stiff leather wineskins, "tied together like the beads of a rosary," which would break the impact of landing in case of a fall from the machine.

The longest parachute trip on record was made a few years ago by an American, Joe Kittinger, who jumped from a balloon at a height of almost 20 miles. But the parachute acted as his means of travel for only the last lap of his journey, as it was arranged to remain closed until he reached the level of about $3\frac{1}{2}$ miles up. Our modern parachutes are round rather than square because air tends to be distributed most evenly inside a sphere, thus giving the parachute the best stability. Leonardo's parachute might have collapsed at the corners. Nevertheless, his idea was completely sound, and he deserves credit as the parachute's inventor.

"THE SAID HELIX WILL MAKE A SCREW IN THE AIR and climb high," Leonardo claimed, if it is "well made, that is to say, of flaxen linen, of which the pores have been closed with starch, and is turned with great speed." Leonardo thought of it as a giant corkscrew that could literally be screwed into the air because the air has what he called substance, now known as density. There you have the idea of the modern helicopter, a good 450 years before it became a reality. To get the aerial screw off the ground, four men whirled the vertical shaft, each pushing on one of the horizontal spokes projecting from it. The outer edge of the screw moves much faster, of course, than the central shaft, and this very rapid motion compresses the air below to lift the machine. In a modern helicopter, the blade ends may whirl at a speed over 400 miles an hour when the helicopter rises from the ground.

For some time before Leonardo drew this design, the Chinese had a toy top that operated on the same principle. Its string worked like the one used to spin a gyroscope top, passing through a hole in the shaft and then winding around it, and a set of blades like an old-fashioned ceiling fan fitted over the shaft at right angles to the end. Because this toy was known in parts of Europe by Leonardo's century, it cannot be said that he actually introduced the principle of helicopter flight. But he seems to have been way ahead of anyone else in thinking of it as more than a toy.

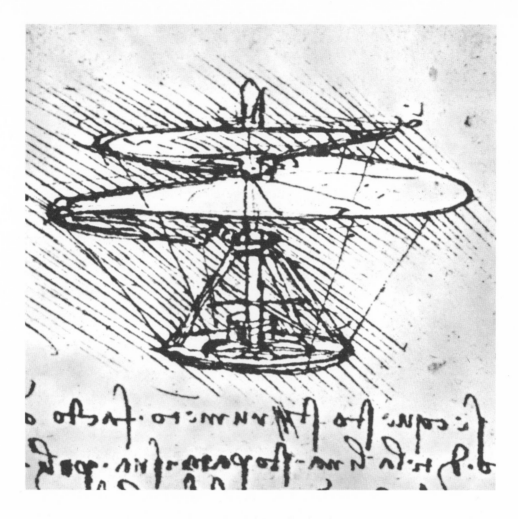

In 1842, an Englishman built a model steam-propelled helicopter, but a full-scale version of it could not have lifted the weight of its engine and passengers too. Almost a century later, a few years before Igor Sikorsky perfected a helicopter suitable for human flight, the Autogiro appeared. This flying machine, invented in Spain by Juan de la Cierva, had the big blades revolving on top, helicopter fashion, to provide lift. Unlike a helicopter, the blades were turned by the air, not by a motor; the Autogiro also required a motor and propeller like a fixed-wing airplane's in order to move forward. The forward motion produced by the motor created the rush of air that turned the blades on top.

Leonardo called his aerial screw a "helix" because of its spiral shape, and we continue to use the name he gave it, combining the Greek *helix* for "spiral" with *pteron* for "wing." If you're a dinosaur fan, you've probably come across the "wing" word in "pterodactyl," the flying dinosaur.

HOME

"If you would keep healthy, follow this regimen: do not eat unless you feel inclined, and sup lightly; chew well, and let what you take be well cooked and simple."

A hundred years ago, it was not unusual to get up in the morning and find steak, chicken, or oysters on the breakfast table. Now, many people skip breakfast entirely or simply drink a cup of coffee. Sandwiches often take the place of what used to be a serious midday meal, and even dinner has been cut down from the many courses it used to include: the old-time "side dish," generally a delicate meat or fish with sauce, would now make the main course of dinner instead of merely supplementing the fish and meat courses. Despite this very noticeable decline in the amount we eat, we are frequently urged by specialists in nutrition to eat even less, because so many Americans weigh more than they should to maintain good health. In one recent period of only six years, the recommended daily diet for a typical man dropped by about 300 calories; for a typical woman, the drop was 200 calories.

To understand why the typical American man and woman need so much less to eat than they used to, we have only to look around a typical American home. The kitchen has a gas or electric stove, an automatic refrigerator, and machines to wash the clothes and the dishes. The bathroom has hot and cold running water; in the closet you'll find a vacuum cleaner and clothes made of fabrics that need no ironing; in the cellar, you'll see an automatic furnace, and you'll see a power lawn mower and one or more cars in the garage. A century ago, the kitchen stove usually burned wood or coal that had to be carried from an outside shed or the coalbin; the family cooled food with ice from the icehouse or by storing the food in the cool cellar or well. Baths were taken in a tub filled with water drawn from the well or by a pump handle in the kitchen. The closet was most often a separate piece of furniture called a wardrobe, which contained clothes to be scrubbed by hand; fireplaces or potbellied stoves heated the house; and the "garage" housed a horse and wagon or buggy. The difference in the amount of housework, in terms of energy, added up to many hundreds of calories a day.

Housekeeping in Leonardo's day more closely resembled the conditions of the nineteenth century than the nineteenth-century household resembles our own. As always, much depended upon whether you were rich or poor. The rich had glass panes in their windows, carpets on their floors, and enough plates to go around, while the poor had shutters instead of window glass, floors covered with rushes or sand, and table service to be shared. Nobody had upholstered furniture; cushions might be placed on the wooden chairs, and the nearest thing to a sofa was the straight-backed bench set against the wall. Clothes were kept in wardrobes or, more often, in low chests. Nor did homes have stoves, running water, or cooling arrangements for food. In cities like Florence, some people had their own wells, and others followed the age-old custom of getting water at the public fountains. As in colonial America, the fireplace served for stove and heating furnace. However, Italy wasn't so cold as New England, where a log blazing in the middle might be icy at both ends, and a man trying to write a few feet away from the fireplace would find the ink freezing on the quill of his pen. Smoking and salting were the only known methods of preserving meat, and people relied on spices to preserve it longer and to cover up the taste of meat on the way to spoiling. It was the quest for spices that inspired the great voyages of discovery, including those of Columbus.

Leonardo tried to introduce conveniences to home life whenever he could. He thought about sanitation in an age when it was mostly ignored, providing for sanitary arrangements in his architectural plans, and designing a handsome bath pavilion for the garden of the Duchess of Milan. In one of his plans for a house, he directed that the kitchen should be placed between two dining rooms so that it could serve either one, and he suggested connecting each dining room with the kitchen by means of a revolving table for easy food service, a fifteenth-century version of the Lazy Susan. At a time when spit-roasting was a standard way of cooking meat, Leonardo invented two automatic roasting spits to save the labor of turning them; one worked by mechanical power, and the other turned by a fan set into the chimney. Leonardo, who lived simply, was a vegetarian.

For his patron the Duke of Milan, he devised a pump that raised water from a local stream and distributed it inside the castle (see section on Water for details); he also devised one of the world's first air-cooling systems. For himself, Leonardo invented an oil lamp to cast a bright light on his papers when he worked at night, as he often did. After burning his lamp until all hours, he didn't want to risk oversleeping the next morning, so he also invented a special kind of alarm clock. ✠

To cool the boudoir of Beatrice, Duchess of Milan, Leonardo devised a large revolving drum for blowing air. His sketch shows two views of it. He explained that "the bellows is always from the center downwards full of water," and that the rotating of the machine causes water to fall from one chamber to another as each chamber rises, driving out as much air as the chamber receives of water; "the air which is driven out . . . by the water," he added, "is that which blows the bellows." Leonardo noted that "this type of bellows is turned by the weight of a man walking above on the steps," but also mentions that one could "cause it to turn by the force of a fall of water," on the water wheel principle.

A Greek of the second-century B.C., Philo of Byzantium, invented a machine just like Leonardo's, but for a different purpose. Each

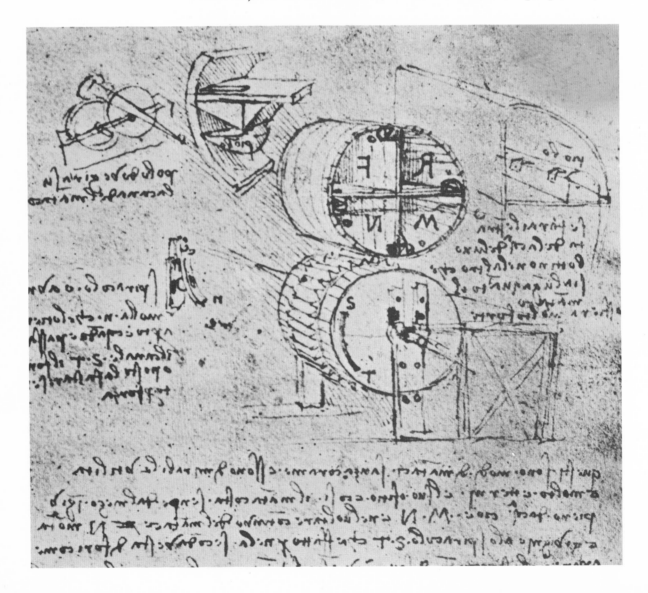

chamber in Philo's blower had a tube with a whistle at the end, so that the blasts of air blew the whistles as the drum revolved. The tones could be varied by means of reeds, and in this way the whole machine served as a sort of music box.

We now have no machines resembling Leonardo's blower, but water continues to be essential to the operation of large modern air-conditioning units. When warm outdoor air hits the air conditioner's coils containing the liquid refrigerant, this liquid expands into a gas and absorbs the heat from the air in the process of doing so. The gas is compressed and moves to another set of coils surrounded by a continuous flow of water, which carries away the heat absorbed by the refrigerant so that the refrigerant can cool another batch of air.

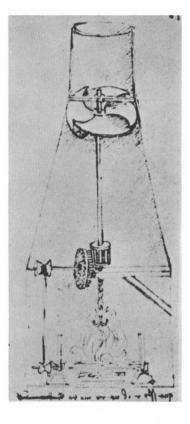

THIS MEAT-ROASTING SPIT TURNED ITSELF and required only the heat of the cooking fire to run it. The hot air rising from the fire turned the fan set into the chimney, and a shaft connected the fan with the simple gear system that transmitted motion to the spit itself. This spit had a beautiful built-in safety device: the bigger the fire, the more hot air it sent up the chimney and the faster the fan and the spit turned, so that the meat never got burned. In a modern automatic spit, we have thermostatic controls to keep the heat at a desired level, but because Leonardo lacked heat control, he found another way to solve the problem of cooking the meat evenly.

The popularity of the roasting spit can be traced back at least to the Egyptians. Without an automatic method of turning the spit, a person had to do the job; he was called a turnspit, and his work, as you can easily imagine, was very disagreeable. At some times and places turnspit dogs did the work, going round and round in a revolving cage to keep the spit in motion. The dogs were not known for their amiable dispositions.

Besides his heat-propelled spit, Leonardo designed one that turned by a mechanical pulley system with a falling weight to provide the necessary power. Its most unusual feature was a device, connected with one of the gear wheels, that supported four upright goose feathers. The feathers, one at the end of each arm, rotated slowly with the rest of the machine and created just enough air friction to keep the rate of the machine's motion even. Perhaps the most interesting mechanical spit of all appeared in a later century. Its machinery included a music-box timer, and you could tell, according to how many different tunes the music box had played, how near your roast was to being done. A spring chicken would naturally take less tunes than a side of beef.

A favorite Swedish Christmas decoration called angel chimes uses Leonardo's idea of propulsion by rising air. Four candles set around a shaft provide the heated air to make four brass cherubs revolve at the ends of crossbars, striking the chimes as they go.

LEONARDO'S OIL LAMP SHEDS BRIGHT LIGHT because water filling the glass globe creates a lens effect. The globe makes the convex outer surface of the lens, the glass cylinder holding the wick makes the concave inner surface, and the water in between bends light about the same way as a solid glass lens does. Undirected light from a lampwick, or any other source, will travel in all directions to make a sphere of light rays. Leonardo's arrangement, known as a toric lens, focuses the light rays into a bright cylinder of light parallel to and surrounding the cylinder that holds the lampwick. If you sit the right distance from this lamp, so that your book intersects the cylinder of light, you will have light good enough for reading.

This lamp, which burned olive oil, was popular in Europe for hundreds of years. Hans Christian Andersen's father, a shoemaker in a small Danish town, made shoes by the light of such a lamp as recently as the year 1800. Unlikely as it seems, however, a German scientist named Otto van Guericke proved in 1650 that electricity can produce light. He filled a globe with sulphur, spun the globe quickly, and pressed it with his hand. The friction of his hand against the rapidly moving globe generated enough current to make the sulphur glow.

Even with electric current, Leonardo's principle of directing light from the source continues to be important. Our flashlights, for example, have a concave reflecting mirror set behind the bulb so that the light is focused into a bright beam instead of diffusing. Most modern lamps also have a light-directing feature.

THIS ALARM CLOCK DIDN'T RING, but served well to wake "those who begrudge wasting time," as Leonardo noted. The clock didn't keep time either. "And this is how it works," he explained. "When as much water has been poured through the funnel into the receiver as there is in the opposite balance, this balance rises and pours its water into the first receiver; and this being doubled in weight jerks violently upwards the foot of the sleeper, who is thus awakened and goes to his work." At least if the sleeper was Leonardo, he went to his work, but not everybody might react just that way. This gadget sounds a little like a remote ancestor of a Rube Goldberg invention. Actually, though, Leonardo could have used a regular alarm clock if he had wanted to, because alarm clocks had existed for a hundred years before he thought of his foot pusher.

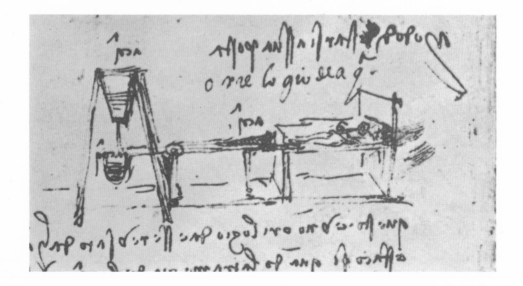

A TYPE OF MODERN CORKSCREW works like this soil borer, which Leonardo designed to make holes for planting orchard trees or vines. To make the hole, you turn the lever *gf*, thus lowering the drill into the earth. When it reaches a certain depth, the drill locks in place so that it will no longer turn. You then turn the lever *nm*, which raises a screw through the top of the machine, and with it the drill; Leonardo explains that the drill will "leave the earth without turning, bringing with it the earth above it." A corkscrew constructed this way pulls the cork by the same mechanism; the only difference is that you keep turning the top of the corkscrew instead of using two levers. When we dig small holes, however, we now use a tool called a posthole digger, which consists of two shovels arranged like a pair of scissors. It may be operated either by hand or by power.

"FOR MAKING A CLEAN STABLE," Leonardo advised, "you must first divide its width into three parts . . . and the middle part should be for the use of the stablemasters; the two side parts for the horses. . . . Now, in order to attain what I promise, that is, to make this place, contrary to the general custom, clean and neat: as to the upper part of the stable, i.e., where the hay is, that part must have at its outer end a window . . . through which by simple means the hay is brought up to the loft." He goes on to explain that stablemen take hay from the center loft at the top and place it in the spaces such as *st* at the sides, which are "made for the purpose of giving hay to the mangers, by means of funnels, narrow at the top and wide over the manger, in order that the hay should not choke them. . . . As to giving the horses water," Leonardo concluded, "the troughs must be of stone."

Efficiency, space, and cleanliness, Leonardo's three goals for a proper stable, still guide designers of our best stables today. Show horses may live in stables where each stall has an ultraviolet-light fixture to attract and kill flies. Feed bags are sometimes served to each horse through an opening like a mail slot in the door of its stall, and the water supply in the trough is regulated by a floating valve that opens to admit more water when the level falls low. The best stables also have a place for the horses to exercise. Leonardo would undoubtedly have approved.

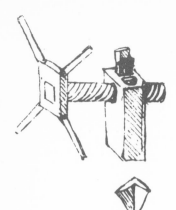

INDUSTRY

"Everything comes from everything, and everything is made out of everything, and everything returns into everything, because whatever exists in the elements is made out of these elements."

American business yearly spends over $100,000,000,000 for paper work, as much as the United States Government spends for all its activities. This immense sum suggests that our economy can afford to waste time, money, and paper; it also suggests new meanings for the words "business" and "industry" in the modern world. Business and industry used to deal mostly with making products and obtaining the resources needed for living: tools and building materials to make houses, textiles for clothing, coal for heating, and so on. Now there are industries that produce nothing at all. The communications industry, for example, deals in radio and television waves; the banking industry deals in credit; the insurance industry deals in finance. And as machines become more and more efficient, more and more people are doing paper work to keep track of them instead of actually making things as they did before machines took over.

Just as the machine now replaces most manual labor, the computer is beginning to perform much of the paper work formerly done by hand. Thus we have two kinds of automation that speed the wheels of industry and threaten to create unemployment. This threat has been hanging over workingmen for two centuries now, since the Industrial Revolution and the machine age began. So far, the problem has been met by inventions that inspire new needs: the automobile, the airplane, and the radio are good examples of relatively new products creating employment for many thousands of people. Perhaps there is no limit to invention, and new products we can't even imagine now will become as standard as our air conditioners and plastics. Or perhaps things will take a different turn, and a new demand for the old-fashioned handwork will arise, once again employing people to weave, print, and make furniture by hand. Machines cannot duplicate the unique quality of each piece of handmade fabric, jewelry, or woodwork.

It might be fair to say that in Leonardo's time the problems of industry were almost the opposite of what they are now. Machinery in the modern sense could hardly be said to exist. So basic an invention as the spinning wheel was then only two hundred years old, and Leonardo himself designed a basic improvement for it. The water wheel turned grindstones for making flour, and there were a few machines for textile processes, metal shaping, and mechanical sawing. But the water wheel was the only important example of what automation means: a job doing itself. As Leonardo observed, "Every local insensible movement is produced by a sensible mover, just as in a clock the counterpoise is raised up by man who is its mover." Only running water was self-propelled; a man had to take care of pulling up the weight, winding the spring or, more often, wielding the actual tool, unless he could harness an animal to do it for him.

Nevertheless, fifteenth-century Italy had flourishing industries, and Leonardo tried to think of ways to make industrial work easier and more efficient. Florence and Milan, where he spent most of his life, were both important textile centers; Leonardo suggested machinery for most of the basic steps in converting wool fiber into cloth. He was also interested in metals, and his inventions include a method of shaping heavy iron bars for use in cannon construction, as well as machines for rolling copper and tin into even strips or sheets. All his industrial machines saved time and labor, but in some cases, like copper rolling, the machine could also make a better product than would result from the same job done by hand.

The most striking example of quality improvement by machinery is Leonardo's invention for making screws. A spiral screw thread is very difficult to cut uniformly from one screw to the next, but it is desirable for many screws of a certain size to be interchangeable. Leonardo solved the problem by using a finished screw to guide the machine cutting a new screw thread; we use his idea to this day. Machines to make tools and other machines, now among the most important of all industrial equipment, came within Leonardo's sphere too: he invented some new tools, such as an adjustable monkey wrench, and also sketched a machine to hammer the grooves into files.

Surprising as it may seem, Leonardo even thought about mass production. He drew a plan that enabled four water wheels placed in the middle of a stream to run many grindstones on each bank, greatly speeding the process of making flour. Like the true inventor he was, he also dreamed of a get-rich-quick scheme; it involved an improbable machine that would grind many thousands of needles in an hour. ✠

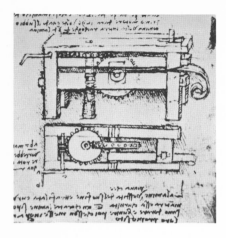

COPPER STRIPS FOR MIRRORS were to be rolled and stretched in this machine. In Leonardo's time, glass mirrors had not yet been widely introduced, and smooth, even strips of copper were often polished to a good reflecting surface. The picture here shows a side view, or elevation, and a view from above, or plan, of the copper-strip roller. The crank at the left turns the nearby horizontal wheel, which has a shaft with a long screw called a worm gear. This meshes with the vertical wheel connected to the roller. A thick strip of copper entering the machine passes between the roller and the plate above it and thus is stretched to be thin and even. Leonardo wrote a note explaining that the roller wheel turned much more slowly than the crank, and thus gained enough power to press the copper into shape.

Paul Revere founded the first copper-rolling mill in America, a great achievement in 1801 when he set up his business. He wrote to a member of Congress that copper rolling had been "a secret in Europe that lay in but very few Breasts. I determined, if possible," he continued, "to gain the Secret. I have the satisfaction to say, that, after a great many tryals, I have . . . obtained my wishes." Revere's most famous copperwork was the resheathing of the frigate *Constitution*, popularly called "Old Ironsides," one of the United States Navy's first ships. He also provided copper for the roof of the State House in Boston and for City Hall in New York.

In modern copper rolling, a large ingot of metal is pressed several times by a power roller; the roller is lowered each time to force the copper through a smaller and smaller space. Glass long ago replaced copper for mirrors, and the steel hull has removed the need for copper sheathing on ships. But the chances are that neither Leonardo nor Paul Revere would be surprised to learn that copper has found vast new markets in industries that use electric wire: industries like telephone, radio, and television.

TO SHAPE CANNON STAVES, Leonardo suggested a water-powered machine that would increase precision. At that time, cannon making began with arranging long iron bars, or staves, around a tapered cylindrical core. These were welded together, and iron hoops were then fitted over the welded bars for extra strength. In Leonardo's plan, the water wheel at the bottom turns two other wheels, one of which is responsible for working the pressing device and the other of which moves the stave along by means of a worm gear. Machinery for drawing metals by pressing them this way had been known for some time, but Leonardo was the first to propose using it for heavy-duty work.

The completed cannon was mounted on a carriage, an arrangement that remained the same until World War I, when the self-propelled gun was introduced along with the tank. That war also produced the famous cannon Big Bertha, used by the Germans to shell Paris. Big Bertha could shoot explosive shells a distance of seventy-six miles.

With heavy machinery now as commonplace as it was rare in Leonardo's day, cannon barrels can be cast and bored rather than being built up around a core. The principle of shaping metal by pressing it as it moves along still applies, though, in such processes as making strips used for barrel hoops or sheets used for oil drums.

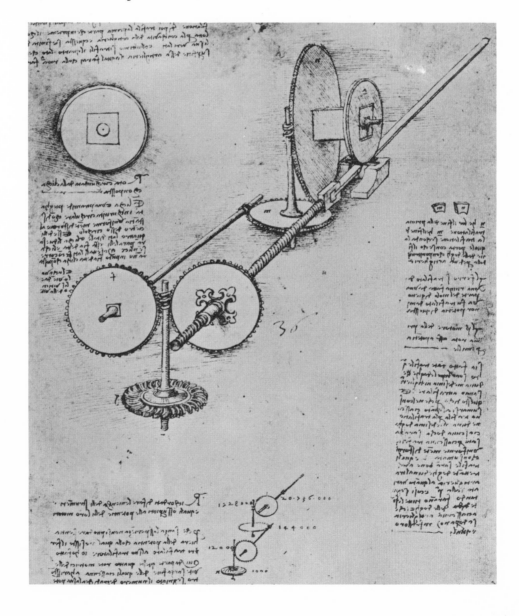

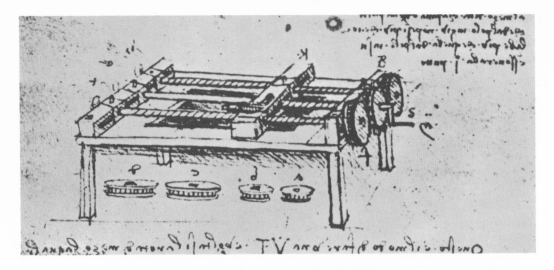

THE PRINCIPLE OF LEONARDO'S SCREW-THREAD CUTTER is still used in modern machines for the same purpose. The screw to be threaded is placed in the center of the lathe between two guide screws. When a man turns the handle at the right, the crosspiece in the middle moves along and the cutter that it holds makes the screw thread. The machine is shown with three gears the same size at the end; these gears will turn together so that the screw in the middle will have a thread to match the two guide screws. But by changing the two outside gears for one of the pairs pictured under the machine, the pitch of the new screw thread can be slanted more or less sharply than that of the others, because the ratio of the gears will change the speed at which the cutting tool moves ahead. Leonardo was particularly foresighted in thinking of interchangeable parts.

Elsewhere in his notebooks, Leonardo gives advice on threading the inside of a wooden nut. He recommends attaching a small pointed cutter at right angles to the side of a threaded screw. The nut has a hole through it, and a strip of metal is secured over one edge of the hole, to cover "half a finger's breadth," as he describes it. When you place the screw in the hole, its thread will catch and turn on the edge of the metal strip, so that the cutter sticking out of the screw's side will thread the nut as the screw turns around and around. Nuts and bolts were widely used in Leonardo's day, and metal screws became popular shortly after he invented his screw-threading machine, a fact that leads some people to think his idea came into use. However, the pointed screws you keep in a home tool chest weren't used much until the last century or so. The screwdriver is a fairly recent idea too; threaded bolts used to have little handles so that they could be easily turned.

If you want to know the oldest method of making screw threads, try this experiment. Cut a right triangle from a sheet of paper by snipping a large piece off one corner. Attach the shortest side of the triangle along a pencil so that it runs parallel to the lead. Roll the paper carefully around the pencil, and you will see that the hypotenuse of the triangle makes an even spiral. A method of this sort was originally used to determine how the thread of the screw should be cut. You vary the pitch, as you can easily see, by changing the shape of your right triangle.

EQUAL DISTRIBUTION OF YARN ON THE BOBBIN is the new feature Leonardo thought of to make spinning quicker and easier. His spinning-wheel design provides for spinning and winding to be done at the same time and without interruption; previously, the spinner had to stop her work at regular intervals and adjust the yarn so that it would be wound equally on all parts of the bobbin, or spool.

Here Leonardo makes use of the flyer, introduced just before his time, and adds his improvement to it. In the picture, the flyer is the piece at the right that looks like a tuning fork. It revolves when the

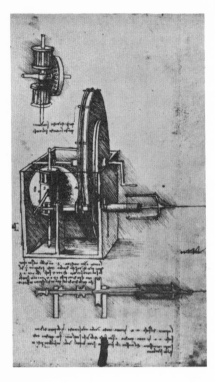

spinning wheel turns, thus twisting the yarn, and the twisted yarn then winds onto the bobbin set on the flyer spindle. By adding the pegged wheel and the two cage gears at the left of the spinning machine, Leonardo makes the flyer spindle move back and forth through the bobbin. This motion distributes the twisted yarn to all parts of the bobbin instead of letting it pile up in one place as it winds.

Spinning goes back at least to prehistoric times, if not to Eve herself; you may have heard the old couplet, "When Adam delved and Eve span, / Who was then a gentleman?" But the spinning wheel was unknown until about two hundred years before Leonardo figured out how to improve it. Before that time, a woman stood with a distaff in one hand and used her other hand to draw out the fiber. The fiber became yarn as the toplike spindle hanging from the loose end of it rotated, pulling out and twisting the yarn at the same time. When she finally got a spinning wheel but still lacked the flyer, the woman had first to twist the yarn and then to wind it, alternating the wheel between these jobs. The flyer not only speeded up the process of spinning but had the added merit of enabling a woman to sit down as she spun, for the first time in history!

One stage of the modern spinning process uses a device very like Leonardo's, different only in that the bobbin moves back and forth on the spindle instead of the spindle moving through the bobbin. In modern spinning, however, rollers do the job of drawing out the yarn: it passes between several pairs of them, and each pair turns faster than the pair before to make the yarn thinner and thinner. A typical modern machine can feed yarn to about seventy-five bobbins at once.

As for the many manmade yarns we now weave into fabrics, they are not spun at all but are made like spaghetti by a process known as extrusion. Such yarns usually begin as a liquid mixture of chemicals. The liquid is pumped into a container that looks like a huge thimble or hubcap with a ring of pinpoint holes near its center. As the liquid is forced, or extruded, through these tiny holes, it immediately makes contact with another magic chemical mixture, also a liquid, that changes the extruded streams to solid filaments. About a hundred of these filaments make a thread that holds together without the need for twisting and is directly wound on immense spools sometimes holding several miles of one continuous thread. The many alchemists of Leonardo's day, who spent their lives vainly trying to change base metal into gold, would have enjoyed the idea of changing a vat of chemicals into a gigantic spool of yarn.

To RAISE NAP ON WOOLEN CLOTH, Leonardo proposed to make the strips of cloth into endless belts, sewing together the ends and stretching each strip over two rollers. Near the rollers at the right, a beam extends over the cloth strips and a row of teasels is set into the underside of the beam. When a horse turns the winch at the back, the rollers connected with the winch turn also, and the cloth strips move continuously, passing under the beam with the row of teasels. Nap raising on cloth is really a process of very brisk brushing that draws out the filaments on the surface of the cloth to give it a softer texture. It is done to many woolens and a few cottons, such as flannelette. Like a cat's fur, the raised fibers lie in one direction; if you stroke a furry cloth, you'll see that it lies smoothly under your hand one way and bristles the other.

The teasel used to raise nap is the head of a flowering thistle plant. When the plant goes to seed and the head dries out, it is covered with tough curved spikes, just right for this kind of brushing job. If a teasel point catches in the cloth during the brushing process, it simply breaks off instead of ripping the cloth, a feature hard to imitate with a manufactured tool. The teasel has been used for nap raising since Greek and Roman times; in fact, a fresco found at Pompeii shows a cloth-finishing scene in which winged Cupids are brushing the cloth with teasels. The Romans also used hedgehog skins to do the job.

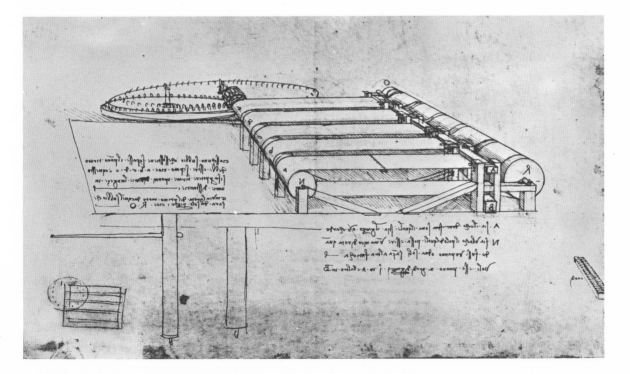

Leonardo made the first known sketch of a machine to raise nap, and the modern machine carries out his idea of setting a strip of teasels together, but they are set on a cylinder rather than on a flat beam. The cylinder and the cloth to be teaseled revolve in opposite directions. Stiff wire brushes have replaced teasels in some modern nap-raising machines.

AUTOMATIC SHEARS CUT RAISED NAP on woolen cloth to give the cloth an even finish. Here Leonardo shows four strips of cloth tightly stretched on rollers and mounted on a frame. For each strip there is a pair of shears that, unlike scissors, get wider toward the tip. The part resembling the top of a keyhole is a spring that holds the blades of the shears together. Through a gear system, a lever is meant to work cords that open and shut one blade of each pair of shears while the other blade remains fixed. Meanwhile, other cords attached to one roller of each cloth strip pull the strips along under the shears; the cords connect with the axle of the vertical wheel.

This scheme may well have been too complicated to be practical, but Leonardo had a sound idea when he proposed to mechanize the difficult and tedious job of nap shearing. A few centuries elapsed before cloth-shearing machines took over. The modern cloth shearer uses not an implement like a scissors, but a long roller covered with slightly spiraled blades. As it revolves rapidly, the cloth passes under it and the blades neatly shear the nap. This cloth-shearing machine is the lawn mower of the textile industry and, in fact, inspired the lawn mower's invention.

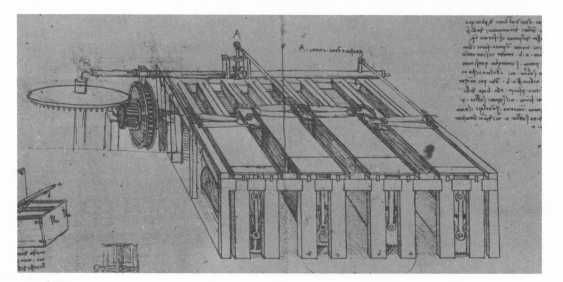

TWISTING THREE CORDS AT A TIME, this machine speeds up cord-making. Leonardo has not shown how the strands of yarn are fed into the machine, but they apparently come in from the left. For each cord to be twisted, three strands of yarn go through a hollow spindle set into one of the three small pulley wheels on the vertical face of the machine. The strands are stretched to the reels at the right; again Leonardo has not shown what supports these reels, and your imagination must supply these details. What looks like a stand for the reels is actually a weight hanging from them. As a man turns the handle at the left, a belt drive revolves all three pulley wheels, and the strands of yarn are twisted into cords. The twisting makes the cords shorter, and to maintain the tension needed to prevent the reels from unwinding, the weight hanging from them gradually rises to a horizontal position as the twisting proceeds. Leonardo sketched both positions of the weight to illustrate this action. When the cords are sufficiently twisted, they are wound on the reels, and more strands of yarn are fed into the machine to make the next lengths of cord.

Many an American seaport used to have a ropewalk for making rope by a method very similar to the one Leonardo suggested. If you have been to the old whaling museum at Mystic seaport, Connecticut, you have probably seen the long low building there in which rope used to be twisted. Such a ropewalk had a carrying machine on tracks; the machine served the same purpose as Leonardo's rising weight, maintaining tension as the rope was twisted, by moving forward on the tracks. A ropewalk might be as much as 1,800 feet long, on the sensible theory that the more rope you twisted at once, the less times you'd need to repeat the operation. As in Leonardo's machine, the twisted rope was wound on immense reels, and more strands were then fed through the carriage for the next round of twisting.

Modern rope-twisting machinery looks as if it might be a welcome addition to an amusement park. The strands to be twisted first travel through a die that lines them up evenly. Then they go into a huge revolving drum with two other revolving drums inside it; the three drums face in the same direction. The outside drum does the twisting, and the rope passes around both inside drums as it goes, because their revolving, side by side, does the essential job of maintaining the tension. All this furious revolving of drums within drums makes it possible for the rope-twisting machinery to occupy a space of about 12 or 15 feet instead of the hundreds of feet formerly needed by a ropewalk. The latest news in rope is nylon. Ropes made of nylon don't rot, and they resist sudden strain better than hemp; they're also stronger for their weight. All these advantages have convinced the navy to use nylon rope almost exclusively.

LEONARDO'S MONKEY WRENCH LOOKS MODERN and works like a modern wrench too. A bolt joins the short jaw piece to the longer handle piece and acts as a hinge; when the bolt is turned, the jaw moves closer to or farther away from the handle, permitting an adjustable firm grip on objects of various sizes.

This design may well be three hundred years in advance of its time. Bolts and nuts were just coming into wide use in Leonardo's period, and the first wrenches had no movable parts: a wrench fitted over only one size of nut or bolt, so that a workman needed a different wrench for each size.

Leonardo also invented a pliers for heavy work; it looked like a modern pliers except that it had a long screw running through the two handles more or less at right angles to them. It worked the same way as the monkey wrench: turning the screw moved one handle of the pliers, thus enabling the jaws to grip various objects very firmly. Another tool, which resembled a drawing compass, had a clamp-and-screw device for pulling out nails. One of Leonardo's biographers says that he called it a tool "for opening a prison from the window"; perhaps he meant to release prisoners of war from enemy jails.

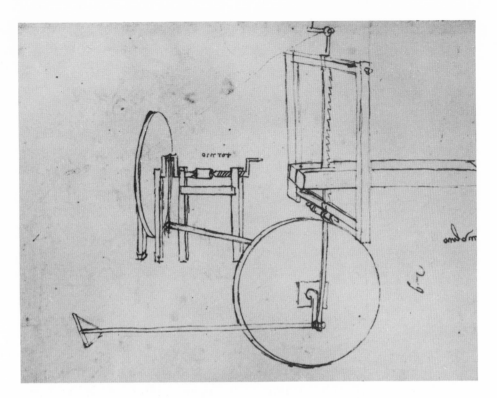

LATHE AND SAW USE ADVANCED POWER TRANSMISSION for the fifteenth century. By applying the principle of the U-shaped crankshaft, Leonardo was able to design a treadle lathe that could turn continuously in one direction, and a saw with an even up-and-down motion. Before his time, and for centuries after, the treadle lathe worked by means of a rope and a spring. The rope connected with the treadle at the bottom, then looped around the work in the lathe and was attached at the top to a flexible pole such as a living tree branch. Pressing and releasing the treadle made the pole go down and up, and the rope connecting them turned the work first in one direction, then the other. The crankshaft had been used before, but never in the way Leonardo suggested here.

The saw shows an even more complicated arrangement. The treadle motion is first changed to the rotary motion of the large flywheel, which keeps the saw moving evenly, and then is changed back to the reciprocating motion of the saw itself. It is interesting that neither Leonardo nor anyone else before him thought of designing a saw with a round blade that revolved instead of moving up and down. Sawmills existed at the time and well before, and they turned by the rotary motion of a water wheel, so that a rotary saw would have been the logical tool to use. But many centuries of hand-sawing probably prevented people from imagining a saw that could work any other way. The early sawmills in Europe converted power by means of an axle with spokes that lowered the saw at intervals, leaving it free in between to be raised by a spring. Leonardo's saw, however, resembles a modern power jigsaw, only a power jigsaw can make over 3,000 strokes a minute.

His lathe design evidently never went beyond the drawing stage or it would surely have influenced lathe construction, which changed very little for the next three hundred years. James Watt made history in the late eighteenth century when he introduced the first steam engines that could turn wheels. Watt faced the same problem as Leonardo: to convert the reciprocating motion of a piston to the continuous, steady rotary motion of a wheel, and he found the same solution—almost three centuries later.

THIS FILE-GROOVE CUTTER SUGGESTS AUTOMATION, as it requires only occasional tending. The operator turns the handle in front, at the bottom of the picture, to haul up the large weight at the top. The weight then begins falling slowly, and the movement of the rope attached to it turns the cylinder on which it is wound. Through a gear system, the bed supporting the file blank moves along, one notch at a time, and the hammer strikes a blow for each move. The spokes of the wheel in back catch and push a bar set on the same axle with the hammer handle, thus raising the striking end. Alternate hammerheads can be substituted for the one on the machine when a different size of groove is desired on the file.

Nobody knows whether this machine was ever put into use, but it preceded the general use of filemaking machinery by over two hundred years. Fifteenth-century files were made by a man wielding a sharp, heavy hammer. He simply pounded the blank, one stroke at a time, until he had made a series of parallel grooves in the metal. An iron file made by this method, or by Leonardo's machine, would be tempered into steel after the grooves were hammered in. Tempering still takes place last in modern filemaking, but in other respects the process differs from Leonardo's plan. A sheet of metal to be made into files passes under a huge rotating cylinder that stamps in the grooves. The metal is then cut to size and shape, and tempered. It would have been useless for Leonardo to design such a machine; neither the power nor the materials existed to make it practical. In fact, even the machine he did design may not have been heavy enough to do the job he intended.

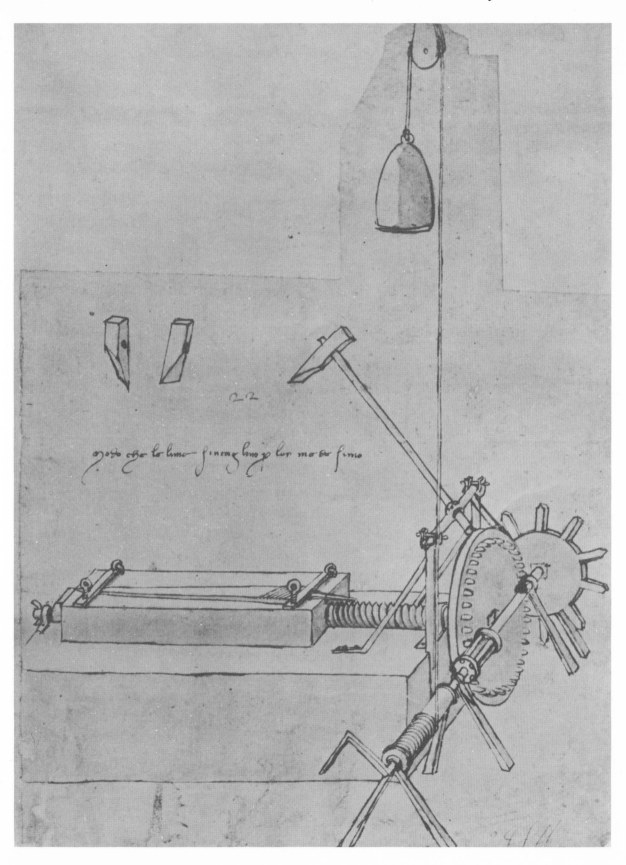

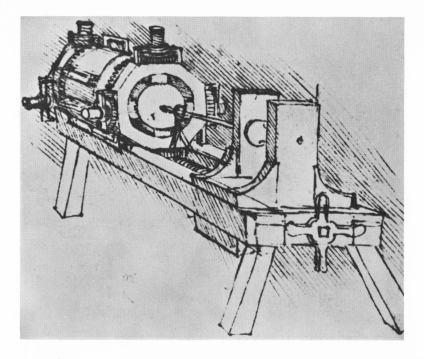

LIKE A MODERN CHUCK, the centering device of this pipe borer holds a log firmly in place for accurate drilling. A chuck consists of two to four jaws that can be closed like a vise around part of a tool or the work to be done, so that a hole can be exactly centered. Hand drills, for instance, have a chuck at the place where you insert the shank of the drill point, or bit; as you turn the collar of the chuck, you are closing the jaws inside this collar to grip and center the bit.

The chuck collar of Leonardo's boring machine is the machine's main cylinder. At each end of the cylinder he has attached a gear, the teeth of which mesh with the smaller gears set on the projecting screws. A turn of the cylinder thus tightens the four screws at each end of the machine and centers the log. The spoked handle at the near end of the bench is then turned to move the chuck and log toward the boring tool, driving the tool into the log.

One method of modern pipe making somewhat resembles Leonardo's idea: after a red-hot steel ingot has been shaped into a cylinder, the cylinder is gripped between a pair of rollers; these simultaneously rotate it and advance it, end on, to meet a piercing tool that bores a hole through it. The seamless pipe then goes through various stretching and finishing operations. For long-distance pipelines, however, the steel is rolled, bent into a cylinder, and welded at the seam to make piping of the desired diameter. The operator who welds the inside seam of this piping uses a television camera to guide his work;

the camera is mounted with the welding machinery on a long boom, and as the pipe moves so that the boom goes through it, the welder, working by remote control, watches the television screen on his control board and directs the welding machinery.

The Russians have recently completed the world's longest pipeline, which carries crude oil westward from Siberia for almost 2,500 miles. The wooden pipes to be made by Leonardo's boring machine were probably destined for a local water-raising apparatus.

WHAT LOOKS ALMOST LIKE AN OIL DRILL is actually a machine to bore logs vertically from below. The log sticks out at the very top of the frame. Leonardo has pictured the log as transparent so that the drill point may be seen inside it, and he has placed the whole drill mechanism on a platform that gradually rises as the drill bores into the log by rotating. The purpose of boring from below, he notes, is to let the shavings fall out easily as drilling proceeds. "And use a canopy," he adds, "so that the shavings don't fall on your head." He also advises starting with a thin drill bit, then enlarging your hole later with a thicker one.

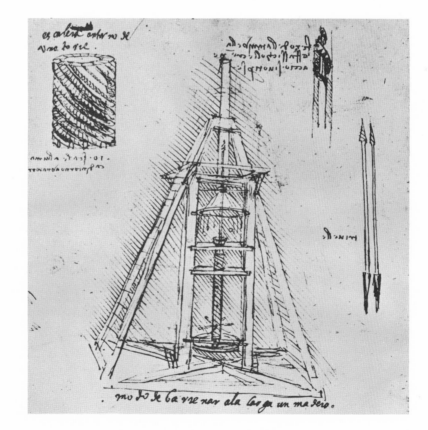

This machine of Leonardo's works the same way as a type of modern drill lathe, except that Leonardo's is vertical and a drill lathe is horizontal. Such a lathe may be used for drilling perfectly aligned holes in pieces to be assembled for furniture. With modern power sources, a horizontal position for the lathe is more convenient, but Leonardo's vertical plan offered an advantage beyond the one he mentions in his note. The weight of the log pressing on the drill point would help force the drill into the log and the job would thereby be made easier.

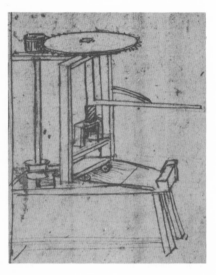

AUTOMATIC FEED FOR A PRINTING PRESS saved time and labor. Leonardo's improvement for the slow printing presses of his day made it possible for a turn of one handle to lower the weight that pressed the paper against the type, and to slide the type bed under the weight at the same time. He must have kept the idea to himself, because it wasn't used until a century or more later. The first presses needed two men to work them: one to take care of setting up the type bed and to run the press, the other to take care of the inking. A press such as Leonardo designed would still have needed both men, but it would have taken them less time and trouble to do the printing.

Movable type, first seen in Europe a few years before Leonardo's birth, was one of the most important inventions in history. For the first time, books could be printed in large quantities. As you probably know, movable type consists of letters on separate blocks that can be lined up in a frame to spell any word needed; after a page has been printed, the type is removed and rearranged into different words for another page.

Surprisingly, the production of playing cards had something to do with the invention of movable type. A person printing a fifteenth-century suit of swords, for example, found it much easier to make a set of small blocks, each with a sword on it, and use them for the whole suit, than to cut out a special large block for each card in the series.

The Chinese invented both printing and the paper needed to make it practical at least eight hundred years before anyone thought of making movable type; they printed immense books by laboriously carving a different wood block for each page. One of the oldest known examples of printing is a little sixth-century sign that says in Chinese, "Beware the dog" — probably not a Pekingese.

Most modern printing is done with type plates mounted on large cylindrical presses, although small printing jobs may sometimes be done on flat-bed presses like the one Leonardo drew. However, the automatic feed arrangement for a flat-bed press now functions by means of vacuum cups that pick up and move the sheets of paper, one at a time.

LEONARDO'S NEW-YEAR RESOLUTIONS included a plan to make a mass-production machine for grinding needles. "Early tomorrow, January 2, 1496," he wrote, "I shall make the leather belt and proceed to a trial. . . . A hundred times in each hour 400 needles will be finished, making 40,000 in an hour." He then figured that if his machine ran for twelve hours a day he could make a very handsome yearly income, equal to that of a banker.

It is not easy to tell by looking at this sketch just how Leonardo could manage production at the formidable rate he proposes. The plan seems to involve a large wheel "of lead and emery," as he says, which can be turned by the treadle below, connected to the wheel by a pulley system and crank handle. Turning the wheel also rotates the roller at the right, thereby rotating the belt around the two rollers. Supposedly, 400 needles at a time are placed between the two layers of the belt in such a way that they all lie evenly at an angle against the rim of the wheel. The belt holds them in place so

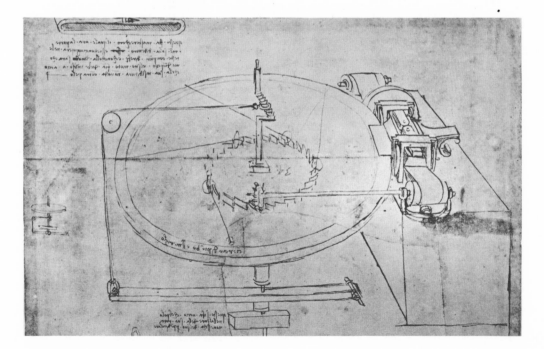

firmly that when the wheel turns and the belt moves around, the needles remain in place, each needle revolving rapidly; by this means, the end of each needle is quickly ground to a point. The needles must have been made of soft iron wire, hardened after the grinding had been completed. The whole scheme appears unlikely, to say the least, but there was nothing wrong with Leonardo's idea of mass production; his thinking had simply gone too far ahead of what could be done with fifteenth-century materials and machines.

Even today, finished sewing-machine needles for home and industry are made at the rate of only 80 to 100 an hour by each set of machines, much less than the number Leonardo planned to grind in a minute. Modern needles begin with a roll of wire cut to suitable lengths, and each length is then ground roughly to the shape of a needle. A special machine presses grooves at one end to make the eye, and the eye is punched out, after which the needle is milled up to the shoulder (the widest part of the needle), the point is shaped, and the steel hardened. Final polishing of the point comes last. Leonardo didn't say what purpose he had in mind for his needles, but modern needles vary considerably in length, diameter, and shape according to what job they will do. The shoemaker, the sailmaker, the dressmaker, and many others all depend on special needles for their work; there are actually thousands of different needles manufactured today.

To make perfectly round coins, Leonardo designed this stamping machine in which, he said, "you should stamp out the round coins after the manner in which sieves are made for chestnuts." He didn't say what you do with a chestnut sieve once you've made it. Here, an even strip of metal is placed under the end of the punch; a sharp hammer blow causes the punch to cut out a round blank. You do not see the hammer or how it works, but its action is like that of a pile driver. The man punching the coins turns a winch to raise the hammer, and an automatic latch releases it at the top to fall of its own weight.

Leonardo invented this method of stamping coins when Pope Julius II called him to Rome for the purpose of improving the mint. Ever since coins came into use, long before the Christian era, they had been made by laborious handwork. Besides being slow, hand operations failed to produce coins of exactly equal size and weight. As a result, it was difficult to buy and sell things with this money,

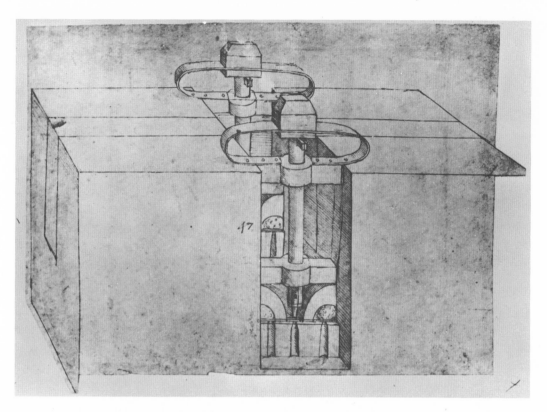

but easy to shave the edges and try to pass off the coin as having full value. If you shaved off enough edges, you could accumulate quite a quantity of gold or silver. Milling, the system of notching the rims of coins, solved this problem later in the sixteenth century. Meanwhile, Leonardo proposed drastic changes in the whole process of coinmaking. He realized that to make a truly round coin with a perfect rim, "it is necessary first to make the coin perfect in weight, breadth and thickness." So he proposed a new system of mechanical hammers to make ingots of uniform size; the ingots would then be rolled into strips by a machine resembling his copper-strip roller.

Possibly, Leonardo's plans for minting were put into effect; in any case they rank as the beginning of modern minting methods. Not too much later, the famous goldsmith Benvenuto Cellini carried forward the plans for another pope. In seventeenth-century England, Sir Isaac Newton became Master of the Mint and similarly helped to improve minting there. A fourth-century Roman, however, had the briskest ideas of all for dealing with coinage abuses. Learning that the mintworkers were conspiring to debase coins, he proposed to exile them all to an island where they would have no communication with the outside world. History leaves us to guess whether this maximum-security plan was tried.

MAPS

"Do not busy yourself in making enter by the ears things which have to do with the eyes, for in this you will be far surpassed by the work of the painter."

When the first astronauts reach the moon, they will have a whole new world to explore, and they will try to learn about its dangers, its possibilities, and its resources. Their exploration will be made easier because of what we already know about the moon, even though it is almost 240,000 miles away, a distance 80 times the width of the Atlantic Ocean. Ever since Galileo first turned his telescope on the moon, in 1610, the moon has been under observation from the earth. We now know that its temperature varies from about 250 degrees Fahrenheit below zero to 200 degrees above zero; we have learned that there is no water on the surface, that there is little if any atmosphere, and that landing might not be difficult on the level bottoms of the huge craters, some of which are over 100 miles across.

Maps of the moon also go back to the seventeenth century, when the great "seas," actually seas of lava, received their romantic names: the Sea of Nectar, the Sea of Serenity, the Sea of Crisis, and the supposedly icy Frigid Sea to the far south. More recently, telescopic photography has come to our aid to make very accurate maps of the side of the moon we see, and in 1959 the Russians sent a space vehicle around the moon to take pictures of the side that never faces the earth. On the Russian pictures, the newly seen side of the moon has a Bay of Astronauts, the Sea of Moscow, and a Joliot-Curie crater honoring the famous French physicists.

When Columbus set off on his bold voyage across the unknown Ocean Sea, there were no such knowledge or pictures to guide him. Nor were there maps for Vasco da Gama, the first navigator to round the Cape of Good Hope at the tip of Africa, or Magellan, whose difficult voyage around the world perhaps surpasses even the achievement of Columbus. We can easily understand how important maps became in Leonardo's time, the great century of discovery.

Florence in the early 1500's buzzed with news of the amazing westward travels of Columbus and Amerigo Vespucci, both of them Italians. The first printed geography book had begun circulating about twenty years earlier. Huge decorated globes of the world showed people of remote lands dressed in strange styles that followed travelers' reports, or sometimes only rumors. The Medici Palace, home of Florence's most important family, had a room with walls covered entirely with maps of the earthly globe and the heavens, so great was the interest in the subject. And no wonder. Maps and globes became priceless keys to treasure: to the golden trade routes leading west and east. Many a ship's captain threw his maps overboard rather than risk letting them get into the hands of a rival country's ship. In fact, ship's maps were well weighted so that they would sink quickly if need be. Modern navy ships still carry weighted code books and charts for exactly the same reason.

As a man of unlimited vision, Leonardo would naturally have taken a deep interest in the exciting voyages of discovery he heard of. Like Columbus and most educated men since the times of Plato and Aristotle, he believed the earth was round, and even worked out a method of measuring its size (see section on Measure for details). And as an artist, Leonardo would naturally value maps, "those things which have to do with the eyes," to present knowledge about newly discovered lands and seas.

It was not only these large-area maps that concerned Leonardo, however. His work with water projects, with military problems, and with city planning all called for maps, and he made beautiful relief maps showing the rise and fall of the landscape and the courses of streams and rivers. Where other mapmakers showed mountains as a series of humps, Leonardo tried to show them as they really were, giving each its own character. "On the tops and sides of hills," he wrote, "foreshorten the shape of the ground and its divisions, but give its proper shape to what is turned toward you." The rivers and smaller streams wind through the landscape, descending as they go and coming together in the proper places. Leonardo could make maps of a very small area to show where a dam should be built, or of a whole region like Tuscany, where Florence lies. Whatever his scale, he used his artist's eye and scientist's keenness to create relief maps far more accurate than any others of the period. Leonardo was the pioneer in the field. ✠

IMOLA, IN THE BOLOGNA REGION north and east of Florence, was
a typical walled city. To frame this map Leonardo drew a large
circle, which he divided into eight compass sections; the heavily
drawn diameters crossing the middle of the city point to North,
South, East, and West. Next to each of the four chief compass points
and the midpoints between them appears its name: *septentrione* for
North, and so on.

This map was the first example of a city plan that showed details
of where houses stood, and illustrated landmarks such as churches by
tiny perspective drawings. Notes next to the East and West compass
points indicate Imola's location with respect to other cities, especially
Bologna, the nearest city of importance. Leonardo may have drawn
this map in 1502 or 1503 during the year he spent working as military
engineer for Cesare Borgia, a man well known for his prowess as a
soldier and ruthlessness as an enemy. One of Borgia's campaigns took
him to the Bologna region.

Besides maps of real cities, Leonardo drew several plans of imaginary cities, to be laid out for ideal living conditions (see section on Architecture for examples). One of these proposed a system of numbered streets, hundreds of years before cities actually had streets with numbers instead of names. When such streets were later introduced, they became more an American than a European practice. New York, for example, got its first numbered streets around the year 1810. A petition to the City Council asked for the opening of a street to be called "the Third Avenue," and described it as "commencing at the Bowery road near the dwelling house of Mangle Minthorne, Esq." One can't help wondering what a man named Mangle Minthorne, Esq., might have looked like.

BIRD'S-EYE VIEW OF TUSCANY shows castles on many mountaintops and streams running down to the sea. Leonardo drew this map with West, the direction of the sea, at the top. On large-area maps of the time North was at the top, but for smaller areas such a standard had evidently not yet been established.

The term "bird's-eye view" actually describes this map well, because only a bird could have risen high enough to see the countryside from this angle. Or maybe a man on a high mountain. It is thought that Leonardo climbed several mountains in different places when he decided to make a regional map. After sketching the landscape from each position, he used the sketches as a basis for drawing one map that looked three-dimensional but retained the accuracy a useful map must have. Quite possibly, Leonardo did follow this method, the same one he used to make his unique anatomical drawings. He would perform a number of dissections of the same part of the body, make sketches of it from various angles, and then create one drawing to show an organ, such as the heart, with all its important details.

For our modern relief maps, a camera in an airplane makes the bird's-eye observation. Overlapping aerial photographs of a region to be mapped are read by mapmakers specially trained for this work. Starting from the photographs, they can draw very accurate maps showing the contours of the landscape, just as Leonardo worked from his sketches.

Though flat maps go back much further than relief maps in history, the first map published in an American book was a relief map. A woodcut showing part of New England, it appeared in 1677. Much more recently, World War II inspired a new kind of relief map. The mapmaker created a three-dimensional model of the area to be studied. A plaster cast taken of this became a mold for a flexible material like rubber, so that the finished 3-D relief map could be rolled up and carried along easily during military movements.

To DRAIN THE PONTINE MARSHES was one of Leonardo's great ambitions, and he drew this map at the right with his plan in mind. The Marshes, a 300-square-mile stretch of swampland, lay in the coastal region between Rome and Naples. Trapped between the mountains and the sea, this land was saturated with the water of streams and rain running down from the higher ground. The marshland not only wasted an area that might otherwise have been used for farming but also provided a breeding ground for malaria mosquitoes.

Centuries before Leonardo, the Romans had tried to drain the land by cutting a canal alongside the famous Appian Way, which appears on Leonardo's map as the long straight line running across the middle, parallel to the sea. Leonardo wanted to recut this canal, making use of the Roman idea to catch the water coming from the mountains instead of letting it spread. He believed that a second canal at right angles to the first would help the water complete its journey to the sea.

Like so many of Leonardo's plans, this one came to nothing. Similar projects in the next century met the same fate.

Only in the 1930's were the Pontine Marshes finally drained by a series of pipelines. This method, perhaps the only one that could do the job effectively, required a level of technology, as well as expense, far beyond Leonardo's times. In the few decades since the land was reclaimed, towns have grown up in the district, and the land now produces wheat and cotton.

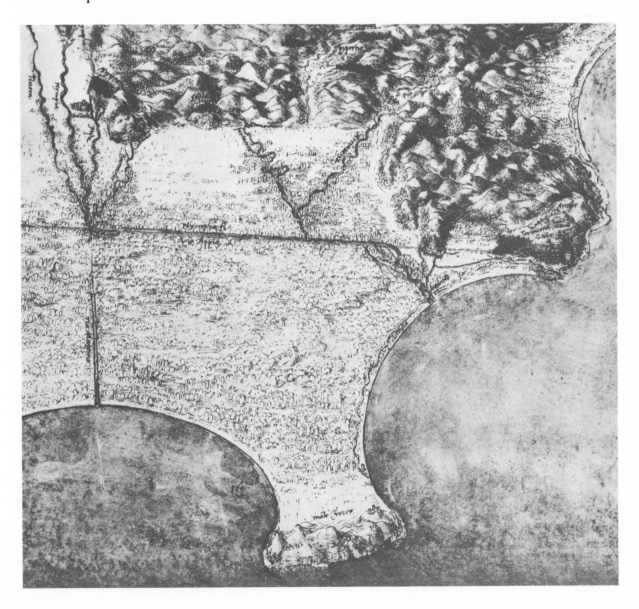

DID LEONARDO DRAW THIS MAP OF THE WORLD? Geography experts have been discussing the question for about a century, and no definite conclusion has been reached. They also disagree about the map's date. Some think it was drawn around 1515, while others put the date nearer 1505. The ten-year interval has a special importance because, if 1505 is correct, then the map is the first known to use the word "America" in describing the New World. Leonardo knew both the great Florentine geographer Paolo Toscanelli, whose world map Columbus probably used on his first voyage, and Bartolomeo Vespucci, nephew to the man for whom America was named.

Officially, the German cartographer Martin Waldseemüller gets credit for drawing the first map showing the name "America," in 1507. Choosing this name, Waldseemüller said, "I do not see why anyone may object to naming it Amerige—that is Amerigo's Land—from Americus, the discover, a man of sagacious mind . . . or America, as both Europa and Asia derive their names from women." Nine years later, though, he decided that Vespucci didn't deserve the honor after all, and dropped the name from his later maps.

Both Waldseemüller and Leonardo, or whoever drew the map shown here, indicated South America as "America" and used other names for what was then known of North America. The far north, or Newfoundland area, where fishermen had touched from time to time, is here called "Bacalar," meaning "land of cod" in Spanish. Perhaps you have come across the word "bacalao," which describes the salt cod still popular in Spanish countries. To the south of Bacalar, you can see Florida, at first thought to be an island.

The map divides the world into eight triangles with curved sides to represent the triangles on the surface of a sphere. There are four triangles each for the Northern and Southern hemispheres, and each group of four meets at one of the earth's poles. The designer has based his map projection on the idea of peeling a fruit like an orange: first he cuts a line around the middle, or equator, of his earth-orange; then he cuts two great circles at right angles to this line, passing through the North and South poles. Imagine these sections of peel removed and flattened, and you will have something like the two sets of triangles on this map. Whether or not Leonardo drew it, his notebooks contain sketches showing that he experimented with this kind of map projection, unique at the time. Equal-area map projections, such as those in any atlas, have a similar though more complicated theory behind them. To represent a sphere on a flat piece of paper is about as easy as making that piece of paper into a sphere.

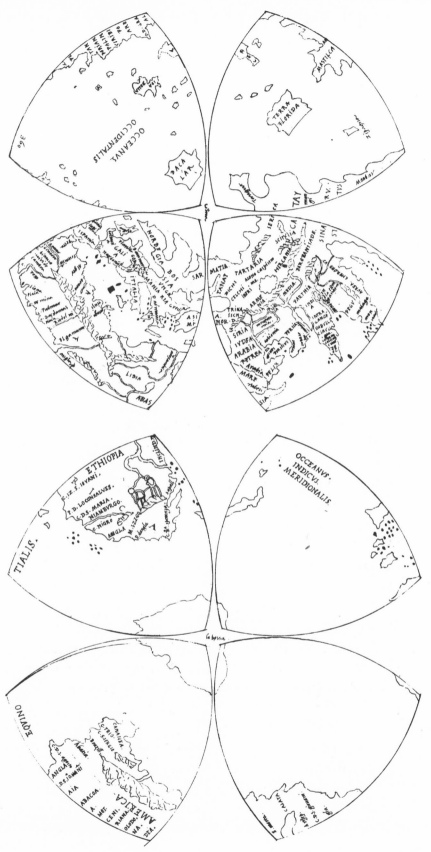

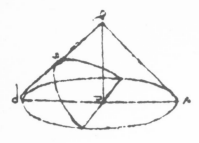

MEASURE

"The point may be compared to an instant of time, and the line may be likened to the length of a certain quantity of time, and just as a line begins and ends in a point, so such a space of time begins and ends in an instant, and whereas a line is infinitely divisible, the divisibility of a space of time is of the same nature."

Measurement is a form of counting. If you hold up a finger, it means "one finger," but it also means just "one." As soon as you separate "one" from "finger," you can apply numbers to anything you like: inches, hours, pounds, dollars, and so on. Our modern computers work on a binary, or two-number, system that contains only the numbers 1 and 0. Nevertheless there is one type of computer that can do 357,000 addition problems in a second; the same computer takes less than five seconds to solve the 800 differential equations needed to find the wing curves for a supersonic-speed airplane. Of course, it has to be given the right program first, and that takes time to figure out. But a person trying to solve the same problem with pencil and paper might need as long as 15 years to do it, and he would be much more likely to make mistakes.

In Leonardo's day, educated men reckoned with their fingers, and arithmetic books had directions and illustrations showing them how to do it efficiently. Considering that deaf-mutes can talk a whole language with their fingers, it's easy to see how the fingers could be used for calculation, especially as they suggested the first form of counting. Our ten fingers, in fact, explain why our number system is based on 10.

Just as fifteenth-century computation was crude by electronic standards, so measurement lacked the standards and refinements of today's systems. In Italy, a measure such as a braccio, roughly an arm's length, varied from place to place, so that a man in Milan reading dimensions written by a man in Rome might interpret them to be a different size. Clocks kept track of hours, but not of minutes or seconds; distance could be approximately measured, but no instrument existed to measure speed. On a ship, a man at the bow might throw a chip of wood overboard and another man at the stern would then note when it passed; often, the time the chip took to go from bow to stern would be measured by singing a familiar hymn and noting what line was being sung when the chip went by.

The instruments for astronomy, unchanged since Greek times, would remain the same until Galileo introduced the telescope (see Optics section for details). Money denominations measured exchange value, but methods of producing money were so crude that the money had to be weighed frequently, especially as coin clipping was a common practice. Little progress occurred in surveying until a later date, and nobody tried to measure such things as the temperature.

Pursuing his many scientific studies, Leonardo decided he needed more accurate measurements than the existing instruments made possible, so he improved some of them and invented more. He wanted to measure everything from the moisture in the air and the load a wire could carry to the size of the earth. He devised methods of figuring mountain altitudes and the difference in height between one mountain and another. The idea of measuring muscle power also interested Leonardo, and he even tried to find out about the expansion of water into steam, something that had never before been attempted.

Leonardo not only applied the principle of measurement to new areas but worked out new ways of making instruments easier to read precisely. So basic an instrument as a weighing scale could be read in his day only by adding up the standard weights in one pan needed to balance the load weighed in the other. Leonardo's design for a scale showed two pans suspended from the ends of a marked beam that served as the base of a triangle; a plumbline hung from the triangle's apex. The two pans balanced when empty, but when one pan contained a weight the whole triangle tipped, while the plumbline in the middle continued to hang straight down, intercepting one of the markings on the base beam. He worked out similar plans for several other instruments, thus simplifying their use.

Leonardo's interest in accurate measurement suggests what we now know very well: that he was a scientist who anticipated advances far in the future. And in recognizing that a "line may be likened to the length of a certain quantity of time," he put himself in the twentieth century. ✠

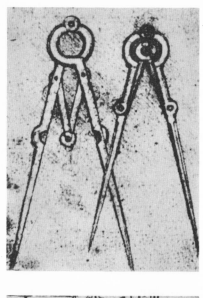

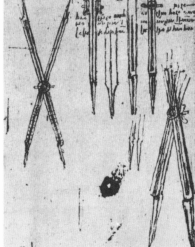

COMPASS JOINT LOCKS IN PLACE so that the legs can be set firmly at any desired position. What looks like a ring at the meeting point of the small inner arms represents a special kind of screw-and-nut arrangement that automatically locks when the screw is well tightened. Some modern compasses have the same device. In this beautifully precise drawing, Leonardo shows two methods of constructing the compass to take advantage of the lock-joint principle. It is hard to tell whether these instruments are dividers for measuring or drawing compasses, as both legs appear to be pointed; a drawing compass has a point on one leg and a holder for a pen on the other.

The proportional compasses in the other drawing can be adjusted by moving the nut along the grooved legs and screwing it tight at the place chosen. These instruments are actually double compasses with points or a drawing tool at each end of the legs so that the measurements of a drawing can be copied in a larger or smaller size.

If you think of proportional compasses as a large letter X, you will quickly see that moving the midpoint of the X changes the relative length of the legs above and below it, and likewise changes the space between them at each end; the lengths and the spaces always remain in proportion. By grooving the legs, Leonardo made it easy to shift the midpoint, so that a drawing could be proportionally enlarged or reduced by any desired amount. Earlier compasses for the same purpose simply had a fixed pivot where the legs crossed, about a third of the way from one end, permitting the drawing's size to be changed in only one ratio. Our proportional compasses today resemble Leonardo's.

Much more astonishing than this practical up-to-date design is one of Leonardo's theoretical notes about drawing a perfect circle. "If you desire to make a perfect circle by the movement of one of the points of the compasses," he wrote, "and you admit . . . that in the course of long movement this point tends to become worn away, it is necessary to concede that if the whole point be consumed in the whole of a certain space of time, the part will be consumed in the part of this time." Furthermore, he added, the other point of the compass that remains in the center of the circle is also imperceptibly wearing down itself and the paper as it turns, "whence we may say that the end of the circle is not joined with its beginning, rather the end of such a line is some imperceptible part nearer to the center of such a circle." Calculus, the branch of mathematics dealing with infinitesimal changes like these, was not really developed until several centuries after Leonardo wrote this note.

MEASURING THE DISTANCE TRAVELED BY A WHEEL dates from Roman times. The middle drawing shows the Roman system. The wheel was pushed like a wheelbarrow and, as it moved, its projecting teeth meshed with the horizontal gear above. By a series of reducing gears, each one turning slower than the one before, a dial finally moved to show the distance the wheel had covered. The Romans invented the odometer, meaning "road measure," for surveying, and it was the first known machine to use more than one pair of gears for transmitting motion.

Leonardo simplified the Roman machine and arranged it for use on a wagon. In his system, shown at the left, the wagon-wheel axle, rather than the wheel itself, would be the first step in the transmission. The horizontal gear marked f is the dial that registers distance traveled; it moves a space of one tooth when a wagon wheel nearly 18 feet in circumference turns 300 times, to cover a distance of a mile. As in the Roman machine, reducing gears connect the wheel with the dial. "On the other hand," Leonardo adds in his note, "the wheel f, instead of reading by a pointer, can cause the ear to hear a sound by means of a small stone which is allowed to fall into a

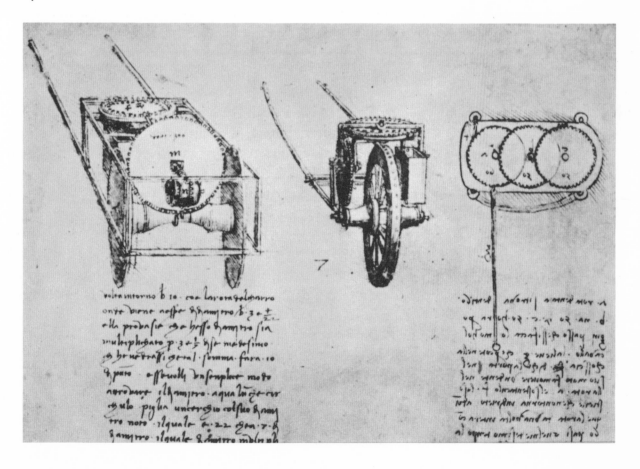

container suitable for emitting a sound when struck." If you forgot how many times you had heard the sound, you counted your small stones at the end of the journey.

Mile counters in modern cars also turn according to how many times the wheels go around, but the transmission system and the dial arrangement have changed (see three-speed gears in section on Power for details).

Leonardo's pedometer, at the right in the picture, works like a clock, by a series of gears attached to a pendulum. As a man walks, holding the machine against his leg, the pendulum swings with each step he takes and the gears turn to register distance. Our modern pedometers work the same way.

THE PLUMBLINE ALWAYS HANGS STRAIGHT DOWN no matter which way the inclinometer tips. As its name suggests, the inclinometer measures inclination, or tilt, from a horizontal position. Leonardo devised it for use on his flying machines. Typically, in his study of flight he thought of every detail. Though his flying machines never got off the ground, the modern airplane carries an inclinometer that works like his; so does the modern ship. The inclinometer tells a ship or airplane navigator whether his vehicle is tipping within the limits of safety. A rolling ship must change course if the tilt exceeds a certain amount, while a plane must be banked neither too much nor too little in making a turn. Leonardo did not equip his inclinometer with an indicator, but on a modern instrument of this type the indicator points to numbers representing percentages of a 90-degree angle. For example, if a ship rolls 18 degrees from a level position, the indicator will point to 20, meaning 20 per cent of the 90-degree angle between a vertical and a horizontal position.

THE MAGNETIC DIP BOARD, at the left of the sketch opposite, is a compass with the needle mounted to spin vertically instead of horizontally. At the magnetic poles it points straight down, while at the equator it points straight out, parallel to the ground. It measures the angle made by the direction of the magnetic pole and the horizon, giving an indication of latitude, though the indication is too rough to be of use to navigators. As Leonardo did not understand magnetism, and knew nothing about the earth's magnetic field, he could have had little grasp of the meaning of this instrument, but it is

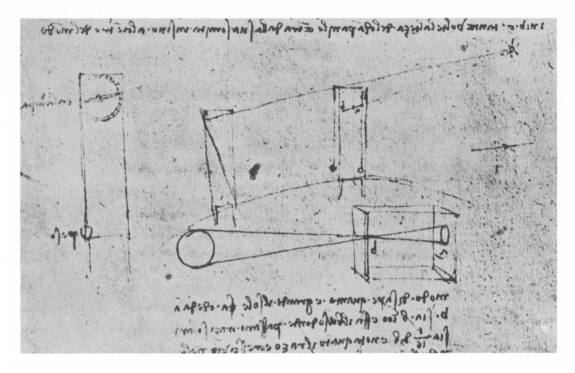

interesting that he noticed the vertical swing of a magnetic needle and thought of measuring it. Spikes on the bottom of the dip board could be pushed into the ground, and the plumbline at the left enables the person using the instrument to set it exactly upright. The needle itself is mounted to swing around a marked circle so that its angle can be easily read; this self-registering feature might be considered Leonardo's trademark as an instrument designer.

We now use the dip needle mainly for the geological surveying that goes with iron-ore mining. When the needle comes near any field of iron ore, it will be pulled down toward the ground. In effect, it serves as a geologist's divining rod.

To the right of the dip board, Leonardo has drawn plans for measuring the radius of the earth and for finding out the size of the sun. The earth measurement seems to depend on sighting the North Star from two different places on the earth's surface, and determining the radius, on the basis of these observations, by a method resembling triangulation. Leonardo's method for finding the size of the sun is more baffling. He tells you to make a box 200 feet long with a hole in one end; the hole must be 1½ inches in diameter. "Then," he says, "note how much the ray is enlarged in the percussion," that is, when it strikes the end of the box. Presumably, he was again trying to set up similar triangles, but the system wouldn't have worked unless he knew the distance from the earth to the sun.

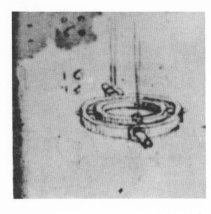

COMPASS SUSPENDED IN A RING REMAINS LEVEL when a ship pitches or rolls. This system of gimbals makes use of an axis running horizontally through the compass itself and another axis running at right angles to the first through the diameter of the ring. The ring and compass pivot together around one axis, and the compass also pivots inside the ring around the other axis, so that it will not be tipped by the movement of a ship. The arrangement shown here is sometimes referred to as Cardan's suspension because people long supposed it to have been invented by Jerome Cardan, an Italian mathematician who almost certainly read some of Leonardo's manuscripts soon after Leonardo died, and probably got the idea from that source. Some of our modern mariner's compasses are set up in exactly the same manner as Leonardo's drawing suggests, except that the whole thing usually pivots on a stand rather than hanging on cords. To achieve the same purpose, others have the needle floating in liquid.

The Chinese probably invented the compass; at least, the first definite record of its use appears in a Chinese manuscript written around A.D. 1100. Sailors of the ancient Mediterranean civilizations used the steady trade winds as a direction finder when they sailed out of sight of land, and they checked by sighting the sun or a star from time to time. The Vikings who touched on the North American continent early in the eleventh century may well have navigated the Atlantic without a compass.

On at least one old whaling ship, Leonardo's idea of using gimbals to suspend a compass was applied for a different purpose. The captain's cabin of the *Charles W. Morgan*, built around 1840, has a bed mounted on gimbals; the ship may rock, but the bed stays level. You can see the ship, bed and all, at the Mystic seaport whaling museum in Connecticut.

A PIECE OF WAX AND A PIECE OF COTTON rest in the pans of the scale opposite, which Leonardo called "Method of seeing when the weather is turning bad." In completely dry weather, the scale, or hygrometer, is exactly balanced. When the air contains more moisture, the cotton soaks it up and gets heavier, while the wax, which is not absorbent, remains at the same weight as before. Therefore the scale tips in the direction of the cotton, and the wetter the weather becomes, the more it tips. The scale is pinned to the center of a graded metal circle on which the amount of tip can be quickly and accurately read.

Leonardo's hygrometer measured absolute humidity: that is, its equal balance was theoretically zero humidity, and the tipping of the scale told how much more moisture than none was in the air. Modern hygrometers usually start from the other direction, measuring how much less than 100 per cent humidity the air contains, and the figure you hear in weather forecasts is a percentage. If the forecaster says, for instance, that the humidity is 60 per cent, he means there is 6/10 as much moisture in the air as it will hold at a given temperature. When the relative humidity reaches 100 per cent, rain falls.

Warm air, of course, holds more moisture than cold air, a fact that Leonardo proved in an experiment: "As regards the proof that heat draws moisture," he wrote, "heat a flask and put it in a dish with the mouth downward and put a burning coal in it, and you will see that the moisture, in order to follow the heat, will climb and fill the flask with water, and the air that was within the flask will escape by the mouth of the flask."

Instead of having a balance system, hygrometers now usually work by a substance that stretches when moist and shrinks when dry. A human hair often serves the purpose. It is attached to a registering needle in such a way that a tiny change in the hair's length, when it gains or loses moisture, is reflected by a much larger swing of the needle so that the difference can be easily read on a dial.

How FAST DOES THE WIND BLOW? Leonardo asked himself this question and invented an instrument to answer it. At the top of the device, he attached a vertical strip so that its lower end could swing over the marked arc as the wind blew against it. The strip was made of thin metal that would respond easily to the wind.

Amateur weather watchers today often use an instrument like this one to determine the wind's force. Official weather stations, however, have an instrument with three or four metal cups placed at the ends of rods arranged like wheel spokes. The center of the wheel-spoke arrangement is fixed on top of a vertical axle, at right angles to it, and the spokes revolve as the wind blows into the cups. The harder the wind blows, the faster the instrument spins. Flashing lights or buzzer sounds for every so many revolutions usually record the instrument's speed, although it may also be automatically indicated on a chart.

Any wind-measuring device is called an anemometer, from the Greek words meaning "wind" and "measure." A recent innovation in weather measurement is the Tiros satellite that orbits around the earth and sends back photographs, weather facts, and cosmic-ray data. Its equipment includes television cameras, recorders, transmitting antennae, and other instruments.

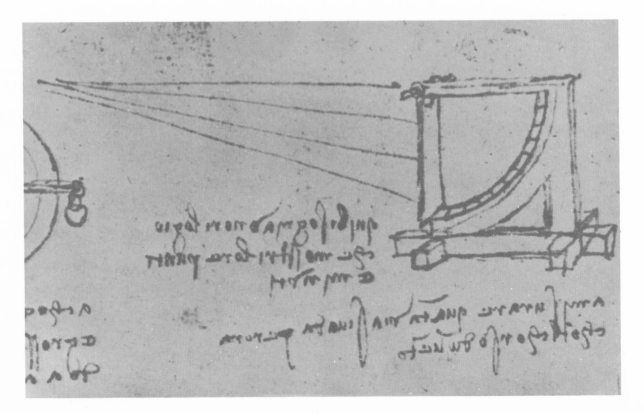

How much does water expand when it turns to steam? Leonardo invented a machine to find the answer, and he may have been the first person ever to ask the question. He balanced a weight and a board at opposite ends of a wire, first cutting the board to be exactly the right size to fit tightly into a vessel a little above the part filled with water. Then he heated the water until the force of the expanding steam pushed the board up toward the top of the vessel. The upward distance traveled by the board measured the amount of expansion.

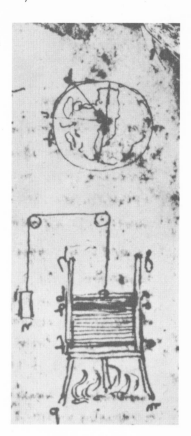

As far as anyone knows, such an experiment had never been made before. Moreover, Leonardo's rising board behaves like the piston of a steam engine. Pistons had long been used in pumps, but this experiment was almost certainly the first attempt to raise a piston by means of steam. On the basis of this sketch, a case can be made for Leonardo as the first thinker in a chain of scientists whose researches eventually led to the invention of the steam engine, and some students of the subject believe that the next developments after Leonardo's actually came from people who had been influenced by his drawings.

We now have a machine for testing how much heat a substance such as a foodstuff contains. The calorimeter starts with a vessel of water like the one Leonardo used, and has a combustion chamber under the vessel. The substance to be tested is burned, and the amount it heats a given quantity of water indicates its heat content. When you hear that a piece of bread or a portion of steak has so and so many calories per ounce, you know that burning an ounce of the bread or steak under the water chamber in a calorimeter would heat the water so and so much. The calories contained in food are determined just that way.

It is odd that Leonardo pioneered in the study of steam but never found out that ice is lighter than water. He wrote, "The more a body is condensed, the heavier it becomes. . . . But if this is so, why does ice float on water, when it is heavier than the water, since it grows in melting?"

"If you want to know the true distance of anything from the sun," Leonardo wrote, "you should find two mountains within sight of each other, which are also as far away from each other as you can arrange and which are about equal in height. Go to the top of one mountain and have one of your watchful friends on the other; at your

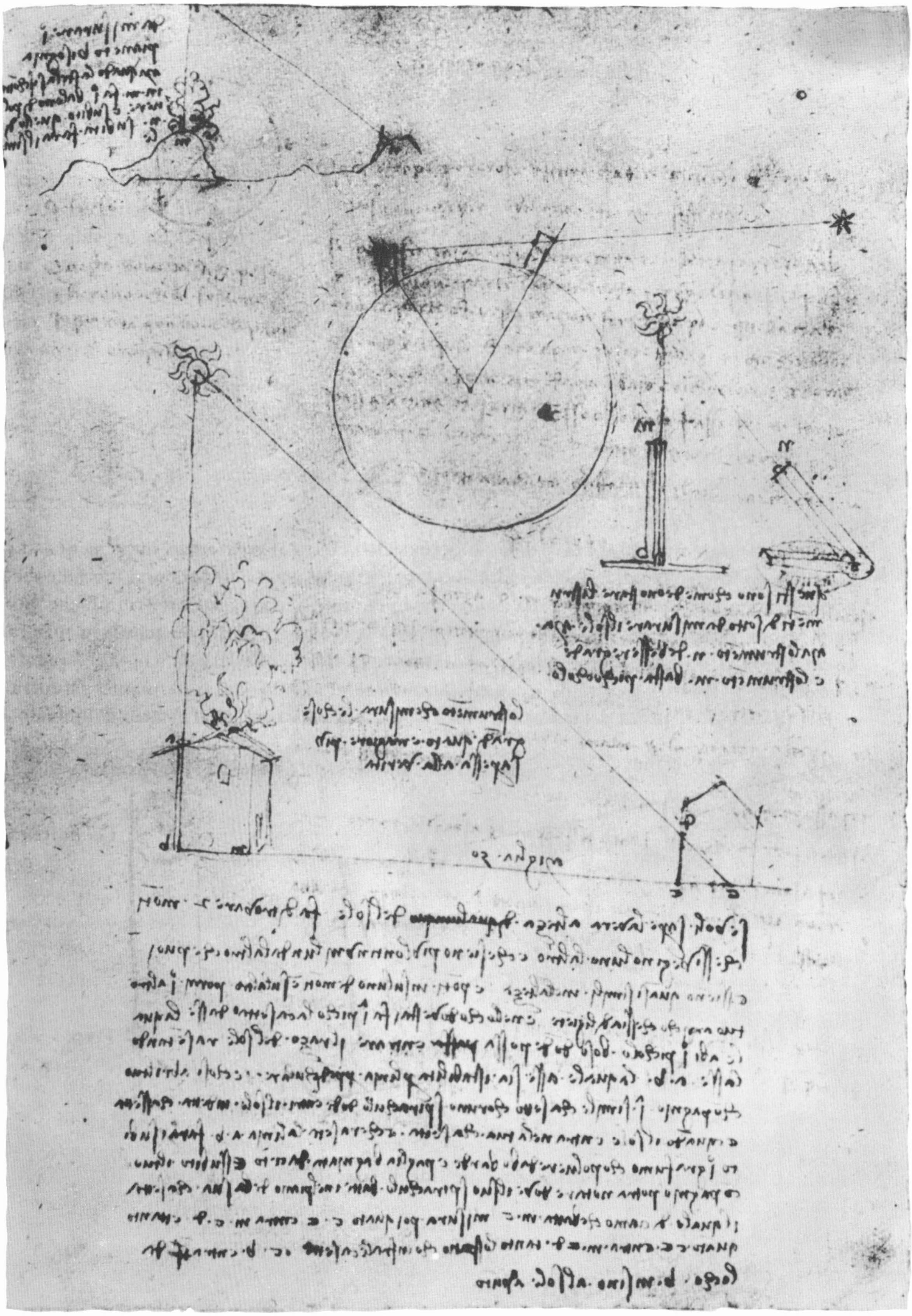

position, make a little wooden cabin with a little hole through which a ray of sunlight can shine straight down along the plank *ab*, which must be vertical. Your friend must have a similar cabin with an opening through which sunlight can enter the cabin. When the sunlight reaches your cabin and shines down along the plank *ab*, you must make a great smoke signal by means of gunpowder mixed with straw which has been moistened in vinegar. Immediately, your friend can observe where the sun ray passing through the hole in his cabin hits the floor. Supposing it hits at *c*, measure how many times *ce* goes into *cd*, and as many times as *ce* goes into *ed*, exactly that many times the distance between the cabins will go into the distance from point *b* to the sun."

Leonardo might have had some trouble finding the "watchful friend" who would climb the other mountain, build a wooden cabin, and wait for the smoke signal. He might also have had some trouble finding the two mountains; a note tells that they are fifty miles apart. However, if he could find the right mountains and the right friend, the theory of his measurement makes good sense. The angles of triangle *cde* are the same as the angles of the large triangle made by the sun and points *b* and *c*, so that the sides of the two triangles will be proportional. Since Leonardo knows distances *ed* and *ce*, and the distance *bc* between the two cabins, the only unknown is the distance from *b* to the sun, which can be found by solving a simple equation.

The same kind of procedure, using sighting instruments instead of cabins with holes, can be followed to measure the distance of a planet, or to measure the radius of the earth. Leonardo shows the sighting instruments at the right of his picture, and says that to measure the distance of a planet, "instrument *n* must be large, but a small instrument *m* will do." The other drawing shows how to determine the radius of the earth by sighting the North Star from two different places. The details are a bit more complicated, but it is again a matter of finding the side of a large triangle by relating it to a small triangle which can be measured.

Seventeen centuries earlier, when the city of Alexandria was a great center of learning, a geographer named Eratosthenes had tried to measure the earth's size. He knew that the earth is round, and he decided that at noon on midsummer day no shadow would be cast by an object on the equator. Therefore, if he could at that moment measure the angle of a shadow on a spot due north of the equator, and if he knew the distance from the equator to this spot, he could estimate the circumference of the earth. The angle of the shadow would have the same ratio to the full 360 degrees of a circle as the distance between the equator and the spot due north would have to the earth's full circumference.

Eratosthenes picked Aswan, in Upper Egypt, which he thought to be exactly on the equator, and he calculated its distance from Alexandria, supposedly due north of Aswan, by learning how long it took a camel caravan to make the journey. Then he waited for midsummer day and measured the angle of a noon shadow at Alexandria. It turned out that none of his assumptions were right: Aswan was not exactly on the equator, Alexandria was not exactly due north, and so on. Nevertheless, Eratosthenes had evolved the right method of estimating the earth's circumference, and his figure came reasonably close to the correct distance of 24,860 miles now known to be the circumference of a great circle passing through the poles. With present-day instruments, we can now make very accurate measurements of the earth's dimensions, and we still use a theory similar to Eratosthenes' to do it.

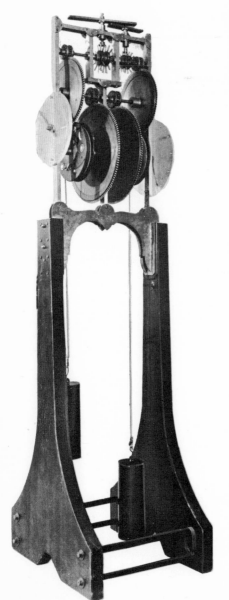

LEONARDO'S CLOCK REGISTERED MINUTES AS WELL AS HOURS, quite a new idea. For this purpose, he constructed it with two complete sets of clockwork, each moved by a weight on a cord wound around a cylinder. As they catch the spokes of the escape wheels directly beneath them, the two crossbars at the top swing back and forth at different rates to regulate the clock gears. The escape wheels, in turn, connect with the gears for hours and minutes, and the motion of these gears is then transmitted to the hands of the clock. It is hard to understand why Leonardo designed his clock to show minutes and hours on opposite faces. To see the time, you'd have to look at one side for the hour, then run around to the opposite side to see the minutes. Although the two clock hands didn't pivot from one point until some time later, clocks with separate minute and hour dials on the same face began to exist during Leonardo's lifetime, and an attempt to indicate seconds was made by 1550.

Nearly all clocks operated by the power of falling weights until a Dutch scientist, Christian Huygens, completed in the mid-seventeenth century the work Galileo had begun on devising a pendulum clock. Galileo, as a young man, is supposed to have noticed that an overhead hanging lamp in the cathedral at Pisa took the same amount of time for each swing it made whether the distance covered was long

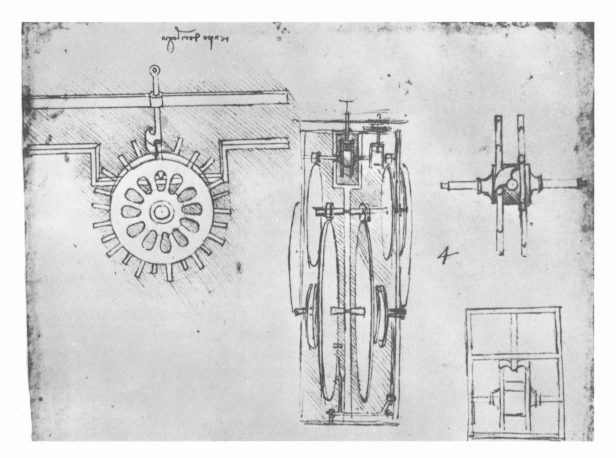

or short. He deduced that the time needed for a given pendulum to swing depends on the length of its rod; therefore a pendulum can be adjusted to beat time. The metronome illustrates this idea.

Time has come a long way since people first began keeping track of it. The first timepieces were either sundials or water clocks called clepsydras (meaning "water thieves"), which might be as simple as a bucket with a hole in the bottom and markings on the sides. As the water level dropped, it passed the markings roughly indicating the hours. In the twentieth century, far from indicating hours roughly, we have some clocks regulated by atom vibrations. These clocks are so accurate that they may lose or gain a second in a thousand years!

But was Galileo really the first to notice how a pendulum swings, or that it can be used to regulate a clock? Leonardo said, "Divide an hour into 3,000 parts, and this you can do with a clock by making the pendulum lighter or heavier." Though he was mistaken about how to change the speed of a pendulum—the length of the rod, not the weight on the end, determines it—Leonardo was right in principle as to the use of the pendulum for controlling a clock movement.

OPTICS

"Look at light and consider its beauty. Blink your eye and look at it again. That light which you see was not there at first, and that which was there is no more."

Light, the subject of optics, is the most difficult to explain of nature's wonders, and as necessary to life as air and water. Without light, plants could not live and grow; without plants, there would be no food for animals. The nature of light and color are still being explored, but for some time enough has been known about the way light behaves to use it in many ways. Eyeglasses help the vision of millions of people who would otherwise see poorly. The telescope and the microscope have made possible important discoveries about the vast heavens and the invisible parts of our world; thanks to the microscope, the causes of many diseases have been isolated.

The latest development of optics is laser, a new method of amplifying light by organizing it at the source so that the rays emitted are nearly parallel instead of spreading in all directions like ordinary light rays. Laser concentrates light into an amazingly powerful source of energy in the form of heat. A needle-thin laser beam, much hotter than the sun, will instantly melt or burn a pinpoint hole into whatever solid substance it hits, including a bar of steel. Laser has already been used not only for precision welding but also for knifeless surgery to remedy certain eye ailments. The beams are so powerful that such an "operation" takes a fraction of a second. Eventually, other uses may be found for laser such as transmitting television programs, and it may possibly be used, too, for treating some cancer conditions.

If laser seems extraordinary to us in the twentieth century, imagine the excitement in the seventeenth century when Galileo first observed the sky through a telescope. Laser provides a dramatic new tool for doing various kinds of work, but the telescope provided a new view of the universe and suggested a new concept of its structure.

In Galileo's century, so little had been learned about the solar system that the Inquisition prosecuted him for believing the earth revolved around the sun. In Leonardo's century, a hundred years earlier, so little was known about vision that most people still accepted the Greek idea of the eye as the source of sight rays traveling to objects and making them visible. Leonardo believed otherwise: he reasoned that if sight rays came from the eyes, then after you opened your eyes you would have to wait to see a very distant object, such as the sun, until the rays from your eyes had time to get there. He rightly decided that we see immediately when we open our eyes because rays are already on the way from the object to our eye, and he even advanced the idea that light moves in circular waves (see Introduction for details).

To Leonardo the artist, the eye was "the window of the soul." To Leonardo the scientist, the eye was a subject for careful study. He made a glass model of the eye to show its parts and how they functioned. Not all of his conclusions about how the eye sees were right, but he made an important start toward understanding the mystery of vision, noticing such points as the way the eye's pupil grows larger in a dark place and smaller in a bright one.

By closely observing smoke, he tried to explain why the sky is blue. Make smoke with dry wood, he directed, "let the sun's rays strike the smoke; and behind the smoke place a piece of black velvet on which the sun does not fall, and you will see all the smoke . . . shows a beautiful blue color; and if you put white cloth in place of the velvet, the smoke is ashen gray." Leonardo believed the blue sky can also be explained by a dark region behind it. We know now that the sky is blue because dust particles in the air disperse the short blue rays in light while the longer red and yellow rays pass through. We also know that there is indeed a "piece of black velvet" behind the sky, just as Leonardo imagined; our astronauts have found the empty stratosphere around their spaceships to be dark, although objects inside the spaceships reflect sunlight.

Leonardo's interest in the color of the sky extended to the color of all things, and particularly shadows, and he also studied the changing colors of objects as they became more distant. The closer an object's color is to black, he said, the more blue it will look in the distance, and the less it is like black, the less the color will change as the object recedes. This fact explains why red is used as a danger signal: it remains red even at a great distance.

He experimented, too, with comparing the intensity of light from two different sources. Three centuries later, light-intensity measurement began to develop into the science of photometry, a very useful skill in an age when we use so much artificial light.

Though he lived at a time when lenses had very few uses except for eyeglasses, Leonardo understood that their power to magnify could be applied in new ways. He noted that the eye sees many stars that look small, but by his method of using a lens system, he claimed, "only one star is seen, but it will be large." Not only this note but his careful work with lenses and the reflection of light in curved mirrors suggest that he had the telescope in mind. ✠

To GRIND CONCAVE MIRRORS or lenses, Leonardo suggested several possible methods. The top and bottom sketches here show how to grind the mirror or lens with an arc-shaped grinder that moves back and forth across the mirror at the end of a long rod; the length of the rod determines the swing of the arc and therefore the shape of the lens. Turning the crank handle in the top drawing, or working the stirrup treadle in the bottom drawing, oscillates the grinder, which would be coated with an abrasive powder, and turns the mirror at the same time.

In the other sketches, Leonardo has adapted the ancient principle of the potter's wheel for grinding the mirror. By means of cranks and gears, he revolves both the grinding wheel and the mirror to be ground, arranging the machines in such a way that the wheel will come in contact with every part of the mirror as the revolving proceeds. Modern machines still have this feature to ensure even grinding of the lens.

It is believed that Leonardo may have invented these lens-grinding machines for the purpose of making a very large metal reflecting mirror for a telescope. He certainly made a careful study of concave mirrors, and his notes prove that he had ideas about looking at the sky through a lens system, something that had never been done in his time. Nobody can be sure that Leonardo had figured out the reflecting telescope, but we know he had some secret project in mind for his work with mirrors. Toward the end of his life, when he spent several years in Rome, he complained about one of his assistants, a man known as Mirror John. This man, Leonardo said, wanted to find out his secrets and tell the world. He was determined that Mirror John should not know what he was doing with mirrors, and we can only guess at his plans. But in the end, Mirror John ran off with the secret of lens grinding and went into business making burning glasses, to kindle fires, for sale at local fairs.

When Isaac Newton made the first mirror telescope more than 150 years later, his lens grinder had a less advanced design than Leonardo's. Instead of the potter's wheel turned by a crank handle,

Newton used a shaped mold and rotated it with a rod that he turned back and forth between his hands. Both Leonardo and Newton used an abrasive powder between the grinding surface and the lens.

Newton made a reflecting telescope because he found that a refracting telescope, the kind you look through directly at the sky, made an annoying color fringe around the edge of the image; a mirror solved the problem. Modern lens science now makes refracting and reflecting telescopes equally satisfactory. Mirrors are usually chosen for the very large telescopes such as the one at Mount Palomar, California, because they are easier to mount and handle than lenses the same size; the Mount Palomar telescope's reflecting mirror has a diameter of 200 inches.

Most modern lens grinding begins with rough-grinding a flat, round piece of glass in one to three stages, after which the glass is fine-ground and polished. The polishing determines the degree of precision the lens will have, and it may be accurate to the millionth of an inch for telescopic work. In Leonardo's time, lenses were fire-polished: instead of polishing the lens with a wheel, it was heated and cooled to achieve a similar, but much cruder, effect. Fire-polishing is still used for lenses like those in automobile headlights that don't need a high degree of precision.

A CANDLE BEHIND AND A LENS IN FRONT of an object or picture inside the dark box would project an enlarged image on a screen. Crude lenses and a weak light source made Leonardo's projector only vaguely useful, but its principle remains the same in the best modern projection machines.

Leonardo got his idea from the camera obscura, a metal plate with a pinhole in it. The plate was set up facing illuminated objects in a dark room; light rays from these objects would meet and cross at the pinhole and appear as a picture on paper placed a few inches behind the hole. "You will see all the objects on paper in their proper forms and colors, but much smaller," said Leonardo, "and they will be upside down by reason of that very intersection. These images, being transmitted from a place illuminated by the sun, will seem actually painted on this paper, which must be extremely thin and looked at from behind." The camera obscura, meaning "dark room" in Latin, is of course the device that led eventually to the photographic camera, another dark room with film in it instead of thin paper.

The projector, in a way, takes the camera obscura and "reads it backward" by putting the light source and object inside rather than outside. Leonardo used a lens flat on one side and convex on the other to magnify the picture. Modern projectors use a lens system composed of two or three different lenses placed together. The combination of lenses corrects picture and color distortions and permits a picture to be magnified as much as 45 times—from a 35 mm. slide to a 4- by 5-foot picture—and in a theater projector far more.

A MAN WEARING EYEGLASSES? The other heads in this drawing appear to illustrate one of Leonardo's studies of the optic nerves, but the face at the left may be a picture of eyes with spectacles. If so, it is his only sketch of this sort. At the time, spectacles were used by older men and women to compensate for the increasing far-sightedness that comes with age. There were no eye doctors or prescription glasses then. People who had difficulty seeing simply went to the spectacle maker and asked him for "fifty-year-old" or "sixty-year-old" glasses, and they decided for themselves how strong a pair they needed. No glasses existed for the nearsighted until a later century.

The first person definitely known to have made and worn eyeglasses was the thirteenth-century English monk Roger Bacon, probably the best scientist of his time. It may be a true story, though, that the Emperor Nero had a huge emerald ground and polished to make a magnifying glass for reading. Certainly no one but an emperor could have important enough papers to justify reading them through an emerald.

Eyeglasses can now be very finely graded for each person's special need, so that optical companies make about 10,000 different standard lenses for glasses. That doesn't count the many thousands more they make to fill prescriptions calling for lenses not included in the standard collection.

THE FIRST TELESCOPE? Long before Galileo carried out Leonardo's plan to "make glasses to magnify the moon," spyglasses had been used, but not to look at the sky. Noblemen took spyglasses along when they went hunting, and soldiers sometimes used them for reconnaissance.

Most books tell us that Hans Lippershey, a Dutch spectacle maker, invented the telescope in 1608. It was two years later that Galileo made history by turning a telescope to the sky for the first time. Actually, a few telescopes had been made in Italy before 1608, though they were probably used like spyglasses, and it is just possible that the idea of the telescope began with Leonardo.

What looks like a picture frame on a stand here may be Leonardo's rough diagram of the essential elements of the telescope: a box or tube with a lens at each end. The long note beneath the diagram suggests that theory, at least, to an Italian authority on optics who has studied it closely. Like the diagram, the note is cryptic and requires interpretation.

The success of a telescope, of course, depends on having a convex, or convergent, lens at the receiving end of the tube, and a concave, or divergent, lens in the eyepiece. The convergent lens focuses into a point the rays of light passing through it, while the divergent lens in the eyepiece redistributes the light rays at a wider angle to make a large picture.

Now, in Leonardo's day everybody knew about convex lenses, the kind used in spectacles. But nobody knew the effect of pairing a convex and concave lens in one instrument. In his endless optical experiments Leonardo must have found out about this principle.

The telescope hinted at in his notes and in this diagram had very low magnification power, less than 1.5 times, but the important thing about it is that Leonardo had his lenses and the length of the tube figured correctly so that it would have worked.

The drawing next to the telescope diagram shows how to grind a concave lens. The two semicircles are the inner and outer edges of a metal grinding device called a shell, and the two rays that look like searchlight beams indicate two positions of a concave lens being ground on the outside edge of the shell.

As for Galileo's telescope, it magnified 33 times; people were so impressed with his astonishing discoveries that he had to go into the business of making telescopes, and couldn't keep up with the demand.

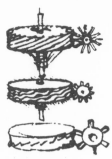

POWER

"I find that force is infinite together with time; and that weight is finite together with the weight of the whole globe of the terrestrial machine."

In a country thunderstorm, lightning sometimes strikes power lines and cuts off the electricity in nearby houses. The lights go out, the refrigerator and the water pump stop, and every appliance from the electric clock to the washing machine fails. At a time like that, we suddenly realize how much we depend on electricity. Yet only fifty years ago, in 1915, electricity was so novel that American magazines were advertising wet mops, oil stoves, iceboxes, and kerosene-burning irons. A carpet sweeper was referred to as a "vacuum," and if you wanted to be really daring you could buy a special attachment to electrify your sewing machine.

Electricity is our most widely used power source both at home and in industry, but it is only one of many power sources at our command. We have the internal combustion engine to run our automobiles, the reaction engine to run our jet planes, the steam engine to run some of our machines. Our fuels include not only coal and petroleum products but natural gas and solid fuel as well, and each type of fuel can be used for the kind of engine it suits best. And we have power to make power. Turbines to generate electricity may be moved by water, steam, or indirectly by atomic fission, our newest discovery.

Of all the power sources and fuels mentioned here, water was the only one of importance in the Italy of Leonardo's time, and no new power sources had been discovered since the water wheel and the windmill known to the Romans. The windmill, a valuable source of power in the flat countries of northern Europe, was less suited to the mountainous countryside of Italy. That left Leonardo with water power, animal power, and manpower to move his many machines. He also had the power of falling weight and the power of uncoiling springs, but these really depend on manpower to pull up the weight after it falls or rewind the spring so that it will do more work.

Starting with such limited sources, Leonardo tried to make the most of them by effective methods of power transmission. The basic methods of transmitting power and gaining what is called mechanical advantage had been known since classical times: the wheel, axle, lever, pulley, and screw were all used by the Romans, and the Greeks referred to these methods of transmitting power as "machinery." So Leonardo tried to use the devices in new ways.

He had one great advantage over most other people of his time. He understood that if a certain system of doing work can be applied to one machine it can also be applied to another. For example, the screw had long been used to lower the weights of presses to make wine or oil, or to print with wood blocks. Leonardo extended its use to serve as guide for both turning and shaping in his screw-making machine, a brand-new idea. Likewise, he worked with the crankshaft. This power-transmitting device, which has the shape of the letter U, had recently been attached to water wheels in order to change the rotary motion of the wheel to the up-and-down motion needed for certain kinds of work. But Leonardo was the first person to see that if the crankshaft would go one way, it would go the other, and he used it to change the up-and-down motion of a treadle to the rotary motion needed for a lathe to turn continuously in the same direction.

Leonardo was the first person, too, to think of new gear arrangements that would make machine jobs quicker and easier. By this means he introduced a basic improvement for the spinning wheel, one that is still with us in principle today when we no longer use the spinning wheel itself (see section on Industry for details). And he was a pioneer in studying the nature and effects of friction, so important as a force that affects mechanical efficiency. Practically, he designed the first machinery with roller bearings; theoretically, he tried to find a way of predicting how much friction would occur between two surfaces of various types, and he found part of the right answer.

His most original thinking about power, however, came in experiments with possible new power sources. Almost three hundred years before James Watt developed a practical steam engine, Leonardo invented a steam gun and a machine to test steam expansion. Almost four hundred years before the internal combustion engine became a practical reality, Leonardo experimented with a gunpowder piston. The water turbine occurred to him, and his roasting spit, turned by the power of rising air striking fan blades, embodied the idea of the air turbine. Perhaps he would be less surprised than we might expect if he could visit one of our huge hydroelectric plants or a nuclear-powered submarine. ✣

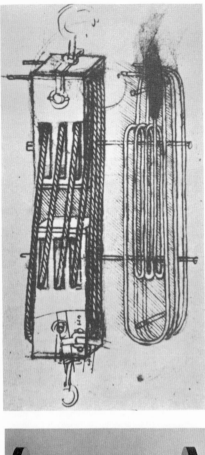

FIXED AND MOVABLE PULLEY BLOCKS are joined in a tackle for lifting heavy weight. The fixed pulleys at the top remain anchored in one place as the rope runs through them, while the movable pulleys below rise toward the fixed pulleys as the rope is pulled down, thus lifting the weight. Using a pulley system such as the one shown here serves the same purpose as meshing a small gear with a large one. In a gear transmission, the large gear turns slower than the small one but produces more power; the pulley system balances power with the distance traveled by the rope. For example, if the rope is arranged over pulleys so that it travels two feet to lift a weight one foot, half as much force will move the rope as would be needed to pull the rope and the weight equal distances.

Though pulleys had been in use since ancient times, Leonardo was the first person to study the theory of pulleys and try to understand exactly why and how they worked. By drawing many diagrams of simple and complicated pulley systems, he gained a knowledge of the most effective way to use them, and introduced the kind of compound pulley illustrated in this sketch. You might see a pulley system of this type used for hauling a grand piano up the side of a building.

"MARVELS OF MECHANICAL GENIUS," Leonardo called roller bearings. When the body of the wagon is fitted over the wheel axle, the roller bearings will revolve against the axle at each end as the wheels turn; thus the friction will be reduced. We now use bearings in everything from an egg beater to roller skates and all kinds of machinery, but nobody knew why they were so valuable until Leonardo thought of investigating them. He was the first person to take notice of friction and to study it scientifically.

In his friction studies, Leonardo recognized that friction could be both an advantage and a disadvantage for machines. For instance, a lens grinder does its work by the friction of the grinding surface against the glass, whereas friction lessens the efficiency of the wagon axle. Leonardo knew that the contact of two smooth surfaces like polished wood generates less friction than the contact of two rough surfaces like stone. He also knew that the amount of friction produced depends on the weight of the objects in contact rather than on the area of contact: that is, a stone of a certain weight would produce the same amount of friction when you moved it against another stone whether it touched the other stone over a square inch or a square foot of its surface.

But Leonardo's most amazing insight was his understanding of the difference between rolling and sliding friction. The wagon axle without bearings, he realized, slid around against a continuous curved surface as it turned, producing much heat and wearing down quickly. The roller bearings, however, turn as the axle turns, so that they merely touch the axle's surface instead of rubbing against it. And the use of several rollers around one axle reduces the strain on each. In automobiles we use ball bearings rather than roller bearings on the wheel axles because the wheels sway back and forth when the car moves at normal driving speeds. The ball bearings reduce the friction in all directions.

THESE SPROCKET CHAINS NEED ONLY A BICYCLE to be right up to date. In this drawing, Leonardo shows several views of them. We do not know what use he planned for chains like these, and they probably couldn't have been made in any case with the machine-shop techniques of the time. The idea of a sprocket chain may have occurred to him after he studied friction and its effects.

Leonardo understood the need for a belt- or chain-drive that wouldn't slip, because a slipping belt results in loss of power. Each pin of this chain has a roller to revolve as the chain moves over a special round-toothed gear, thus reducing friction. As Leonardo apparently foresaw, the chain transmits a maximum of power.

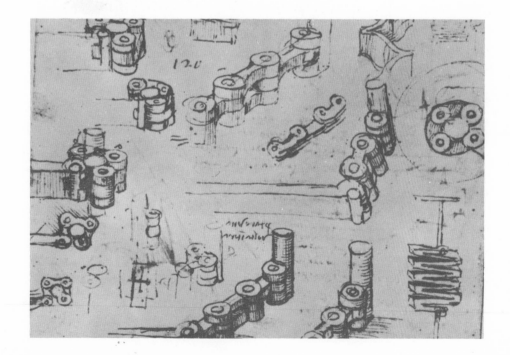

THE CENTER ROLLER TURNS THE OTHERS when it is turned by the handle at the top. The device demonstrates the principle of power transmission by friction; Leonardo may have meant it merely for this purpose, or he may have been planning a machine detail. His tinplate roller, which looked like the wringer of a washing machine, operated by friction: the handle connected with one roller, and the pressure of the turning roller on the tin moved the tin through, while the moving tin pressed on the other roller and made it turn.

We don't use friction transmission much any more for turning rollers, but it can be seen in some belt systems. For example, the moving part of a supermarket check-out counter is a belt turned by friction transmission from rollers. And some of the earliest cars used friction to transmit power. A disc turned by the engine was placed so that the rim of another disc would be at right angles to its surface. The second disc could be moved back and forth across the surface of the first. The nearer it moved toward one edge of the first disc, the faster it turned; this happened because the outside edge of any disc (a phonograph record is a good example) revolves faster than its center. Moving the disc away from the center in the opposite direction put the car in reverse.

CART WHEELS COULD TURN AT DIFFERENT SPEEDS by means of this transmission system that connected one wheel to the cart's moving power and left the other free. Differential transmission, as this system is called, becomes necessary when a power-driven cart such as the one Leonardo designed rounds a curve and the inside wheel needs to go slower than the outside wheel. Otherwise, the axle connecting the wheels will be overstrained and perhaps broken. See section on Transportation for details of Leonardo's automatic wagon. A cart pulled by a horse doesn't require a differential system because each wheel moves separately at the end of its axle, but when the power is part of the cart it naturally has to connect with the wheels in order to turn them.

For the modern automobile, the differential becomes an even more complicated problem than it was for Leonardo's cart. At the speeds automobiles travel, the power must be connected with both back wheels, not just one, or the driver could never keep the car straight on the road. So the transmission system has to provide separate controls for the wheels instead of leaving one free to go at its own speed. Because the designers of the first gasoline-powered cars had not yet solved the details of this problem, the cars frequently suffered broken axles. A solution has now been found that makes the broken axle a thing of the past, but Leonardo was remarkably foresighted to deal with a problem that would become serious four hundred years after his time.

LEONARDO'S GEAR TRANSMISSION MOVED AT THREE SPEEDS, all the gears turning together. The mile-counting system in a car uses a set of gears that turn at different rates this way. In a car, numbers from 0 to 9 appear on the rim of each gear, and the gears move in ratios of 1 to 10: that is, the top gear, which turns fastest, indicates tenths of a mile, the middle gear miles, and the bottom gear 10-mile units. The power to turn the mile-counter gears comes from a metal strip inside a flexible tube, all connected with the car's front wheel.

Cars with a gearshift moved by the driver have a gear-transmission arrangement resembling Leonardo's in that the gears are different sizes and therefore turn at different rates; but, unlike his design, only one of these gears at a time is connected with the engine. When the driver shifts gears, he disengages one gear and engages another to change the ratio between the speed of the engine and the speed of the wheels.

Leonardo did not explain his purpose for a gear system that ran at several speeds. The model represents a theoretical study, and, as usual, Leonardo was probably dealing with an idea that would be needed in the future more than in his own time.

Two VIEWS OF A MOTOR show Leonardo's modern approach to draftsmanship. At the left, he drew the motor assembled for operation, while at the right, he sketched its parts ready for assembly. A falling weight turns a shaft that connects with the two sets of wheels through a cage gear, one of Leonardo's favorite transmission methods. When the motor is assembled, the spokes of the cage gear catch, one by one, the pegs on the outer wheels. The triangular projection on each inner wheel catches the teeth inside the rim of the outer wheel to make a ratchet device that regulates the speed of the motor, serving the same purpose as the escapement of a clock (see section on

Measure for details of Leonardo's clock). The small upright shaft at the right-hand side of the assembled motor would also be turning at an even speed, and would be hooked up with whatever tool Leonardo planned the motor to operate.

Modern power sources bring with them their own devices for keeping motor speed constant; the fixed-speed electric motor and the governor now do this job, which becomes necessary when a machine must deal with a variable load. An air-conditioning machine, for instance, has a heavier load as the outside air gets hotter, because more power is needed to cool the same quantity of air. To compensate for this variable load and keep your room temperature at a constant level, the motor of the air-conditioner is built so that it automatically draws more current as the outdoor temperature rises. Otherwise, the speed and therefore the effectiveness of the machine would go down as its load went up, a point Leonardo seems to have understood.

THESE SPECIALLY SHAPED GEAR TEETH WEAR BETTER than the usual straight, or spur, cog teeth, particularly when machinery moves at high speeds. The teeth twist like a screw thread around the rim of each gear, and because of this slightly spiral shape they are called helical gear teeth. When the gears turn, the helical teeth meet in such a way that they touch with an overlapping action that reduces noise and lost motion in a gear transmission. As Leonardo said, they last longer because "their contact is larger." Helical gears are often used to transform the very fast motion of a power generator such as a turbine to the much slower motion needed for a powerful driving shaft like the one that turns a ship's propeller. Leonardo never had to deal with machinery turning at anything like modern speeds, but he nevertheless took notice of the problem.

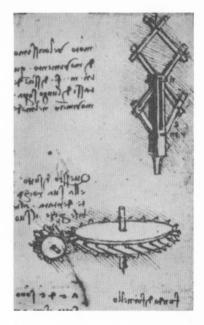

The gadget sketched above the gears is a type of cutting or grasping implement used to deal with objects out of reach. For instance, a gardener could—and sometimes still does—use it to prune the branch of a tree, or it could be used on a boat to fish out something that falls overboard. By bringing together the ends of the arms at *f*, the user elongates the whole frame and at the same time closes the small blades at the bottom. Pushing the arms apart, of course, does the reverse. Anybody who has used a pantograph for making an enlarged copy of a drawing will be familiar with this kind of movable frame.

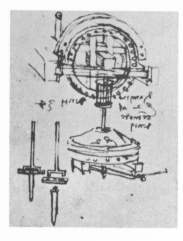

THIS BAND BRAKE COULD STOP THE MILLSTONE from turning. For centuries, millstones to grind grain were moved by power transmitted from water wheels. Without a braking mechanism, the upper stone would never stop turning, because of the continuous flow of the millstream over or under the water wheel. Here the grindstone, shown at the bottom of the drawing, is moved by a vertical shaft from the large toothed wheel at the top; this wheel connects by a horizontal shaft with the water wheel, which does not appear in the picture. The semicircular band above the toothed wheel may be lowered by the lever at the left so that its pressure against the wheel rim will stop the upper wheel, and therefore the millstone below, from turning.

James Watt's first successful steam engine, built in 1782, opened the age of power mills when it was installed to turn a grindstone at Dartmouth, England. And now the old millstreams and grindstones have given way to electric power and steel rollers, although the finest flours are still stone-ground. But if you look into the inner structure of a car, you'll see a modern version of Leonardo's band brake. The brake consists of two semicircular bands of flexible steel which surround a drum on the axle near the wheel. These bands almost join at their ends to make a complete circle. When the driver steps on his brake pedal, he generates hydraulic pressure which squeezes the band ends together, thereby tightening them around the drum and stopping it and the wheel of the car. In principle, this exactly resembles Leonardo's plan.

FALLING WATER TURNED THE BLADES of Leonardo's roughly-drawn screw, causing the vertical shaft to revolve and transmit power. As in the modern water turbine it anticipates in theory, the screw was enclosed in a frame so that the water would fall against the screw and then flow out of the casing. The turbine screw or wheel is a cross between the vertical overshot water wheel, turned by falling water, and the horizontal water wheel, set underwater (see cannon-stave shaper in section on Industry for example). But a given amount of falling water can be more effectively used by the turbine than by the overshot water wheel. The horizontal water wheel makes the least effective use of water unless the water flow can be directed at the wheel through a pipe. About seventy-five years after Leonardo drew this sketch, a partially enclosed turbinelike wheel had been introduced, but Leonardo's design actually comes nearer to the ac-

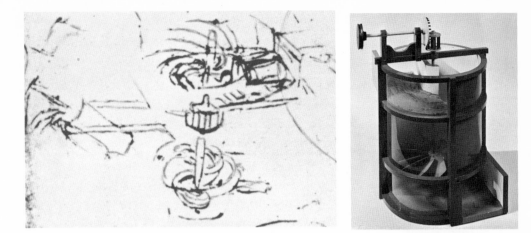

tion of a true turbine, which didn't come along until almost four hundred years after his time.

A modern water turbine may run at speeds up to 1,000 revolutions per minute. Its main use is to generate electric power; in other words, the water acts as what we call the prime mover, operating the turbine to make the electricity for doing the actual work. So if you live in an area near one of the great hydroelectric plants, the power that lights your house and runs your machines can be traced back to water rushing through a large pipe. Other areas use steam turbines; coal serves as the prime mover, heating the water to make steam. Lacking electricity, Leonardo naturally intended this turbine to do work rather than using it as we do today to create another type of power.

IT WORKS LIKE A CUPPING GLASS, Leonardo said of his method of lifting a weight by means of a gunpowder explosion. In his day, doctors used a cupping glass to try to draw infections to the surface of the body; as a matter of fact, the cupping glass was used until quite recently in some countries as a treatment at certain stages of pneumonia. This glass, something like an eyecup, was heated by rubbing it with alcohol and lighting a match inside it, after which it was immediately applied to the skin. Lighting the match to the alcohol used up the oxygen, thus creating a partial vacuum inside the glass. When the glass was quickly pressed against the skin, the vacuum had the effect of drawing the skin inside the rim of the glass, bringing blood to the surface of the skin. Doctors also used the cupping glass to draw blood, a favorite cure for almost any ailment in Leonardo's day.

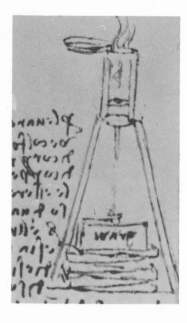

Leonardo tried to apply the idea of suction by vacuum to the problem of lifting a heavy weight. To do so, he suspended the weight from a piston rod and fitted a cylinder on top of the piston. The weight rests on a sort of bellows made of heavy leather. Then he touched off gunpowder inside the cylinder, as if he were dealing with a huge cupping glass; the cylinder "should be lit from below like a bombard [a mortar]," he says, "and the touch-hole rapidly closed and [the cylinder] immediately closed on top." In this way a partial vacuum will be created in the cylinder, supposedly having the power to draw up the piston and the weight hanging from it, and also causing the leather bellows to rise below the weight. The only apparent reason for the bellows seems to be to let the weight down more gently than it would otherwise drop.

It is true that a suction pump raises water by creating a vacuum above it, but Leonardo's method would hardly have created a vacuum powerful enough to lift a heavy weight. If he had used the gunpowder explosion as a direct force under the piston instead of as an indirect force above it, he would have been working with a primitive version of the internal combustion engine that runs cars and other motors. Impractical as his weight-raising plan seems to have been, Leonardo was looking into the future when he thought of an explosion as a source of power.

AIR STREAM FROM BELLOWS TURNS THE WHEEL, which transmits power to do work. In the sketch at right, the power transmission goes around the four sides of a square, returning finally to the wheel moved by the air stream. The arrangement of wheels turning wheels without getting a useful job done indicates that Leonardo drew the picture to illustrate a principle rather than as part of a proposed machine. The principle involved, of course, is that of a turbine wheel running on compressed air. Unfortunately, the sketch doesn't make clear how Leonardo intended to run the bellows; this problem still applies to the use of compressed air as a power source. By means of dams and pipes, running water can become a powerful force to move turbine wheels, and once the dam installation is complete, the water takes care of itself. Compressed air, however, must be produced artificially in order to become a source of power. It is therefore always a secondary power source, requiring a pumping mechanism of some kind to make it.

Modern city dwellers are perhaps more familiar than they would care to be with the thunderous air drills that make holes in the streets just below their windows. The drills run on compressed air, supplied through Diesel-operated pumps, because electric motors built into the drills themselves would make them too heavy to handle. Compressed air also operates the brakes in many trucks and trains. A few portable tools get their power from air turbines, but the air turbine cannot be compared with the water or steam turbine as an important source of power. The windmills of Leonardo's time worked on somewhat the same theory except that they made use of naturally moving air that did not need to be directed in a strong, narrow stream.

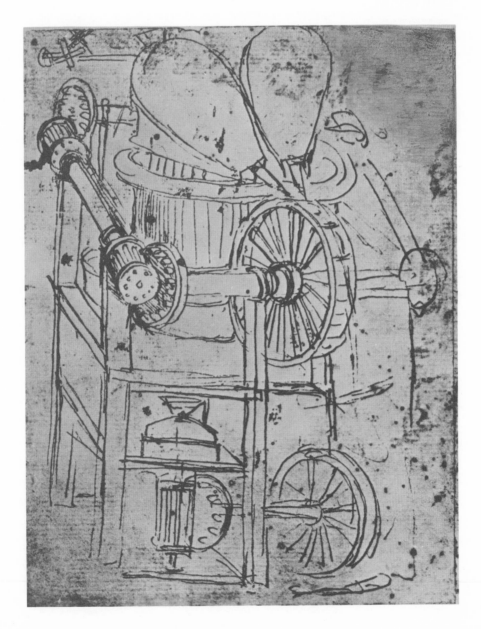

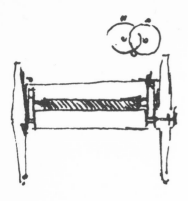

TRANSPORTATION

"When you wish to know the quantity of the force that is required in order to drag the same weight over beds of different slope, you have to make the experiment and ascertain what amount of force is required to move the weight along a level road, that is, to ascertain the nature of its friction."

Measured in feet, the length of a mile never varies; measured in time, it changes drastically. The same mile may be twenty minutes long for the person on foot and a fraction of a second long for the astronaut in his spaceship. The Pilgrims needed two months to cross the Atlantic Ocean, but supersonic airplanes may soon be crossing the Atlantic in two hours.

Distance translated into time thus tells the history of transportation, and that history has developed faster in the last century than in all the previous centuries combined. If all gasoline-powered vehicles suddenly disappeared, life in the suburban and rural areas of America would be paralyzed and city life would also be seriously affected: most people would not be able to get to their jobs, much farm work would stop, and deliveries would be so sharply reduced that America's abundance would quickly seem to vanish. If all airplanes disappeared too, business and government would find it difficult to conduct their affairs, and our world organization, the United Nations, could hardly function effectively. Clearly, our new forms of transportation are a key to much of the modern world's activity.

Air and road transportation dominate twentieth-century life, but in the fifteenth century, sea transportation was the vital thing. Business depended on the sea for its commerce, and sea travel led to the discovery of new continents; mastery of the sea meant riches and political advantages. Looking back from our era of steam- and Diesel-powered ships, we cannot easily realize that until the fifteenth century no one had ever thought of putting more than one mast on a sailing vessel and that ships under sail mostly depended on a following wind to move them. It is true that the Vikings had sailed great distances in their primitive ships, but the decisive exploration of the globe came from the Mediterranean countries. Portugal took the lead in voyages of discovery, and Italy took the lead in developing navigation into a science; it was from Mediterranean trade with the

Italians that the Portuguese learned enough navigation to venture boldly into the unknown and frightening Atlantic Ocean.

Observing the wagons and ships for land and sea travel, Leonardo noticed some of their defects, and his penetrating mind discovered ways to improve them. His detailed studies of the movements of water had taught him much about the best shape for a ship's hull, to achieve the most efficient passage through the water. At least one sketch in his notebooks proves that he understood the principle of streamlining at a time when the typical sailing ship had a decidedly tubby appearance. Leonardo also thought about the comparative movement of the ship and the water; unlike land vehicles, which travel on fixed roads, a ship moves through water that is itself moved by winds, currents, and tides. The ship's rudder could be improved too, he decided, by connecting it to the tiller through a worm gear, thus making it easier for the steersman to turn the heavy rudder of a large ship from side to side.

Leonardo applied his friction studies to wagon wheels (see roller bearings in section on Power for details) and to the problem of wheels traveling along a road, recognizing that he must know the force "required to move the weight along a level road" before he could deal with "beds of different slope." The effect of the wheel's size on its efficiency also concerned him. He understood that a larger wheel would turn more easily than a small one on a rough road, and when he visited a certain section of Italy where he saw carts with small wheels, he wrote himself a note about the stupidity of their design.

Perhaps Leonardo's most famous scientific work dealt with transportation through the air. Others before him had thought of aviation as a possibility, but he was the first to attempt to analyze the problem systematically. The section on Flight discusses this subject more fully.

If the investigation of flight was Leonardo's most famous work, his thoughts about mechanizing transportation are just as remarkable. In his sketch of a wagon containing its own power for turning the wheels, he foresaw the invention of the automobile; sketching boats propelled by paddle wheels, he anticipated the age of the steamboat. And his notebooks include a picture of an armored tank, a war vehicle not extensively used until World War I. ✠

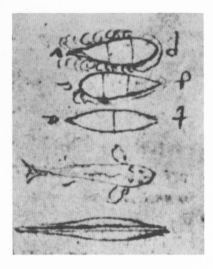

THE SHAPE OF FISH SUGGESTED A STREAMLINED HULL for ships to move more quickly through the water. The note accompanying this sketch says: "These three ships of uniform breadth, length and depth, when propelled by equal powers will have different speed of movement; for the ship that presents its widest part in front is swifter, and it resembles the shape of birds and fishes such as the mullet. And this ship opens with its side and in front of it a great quantity of water, which afterwards with its revolutions presses against the last two-thirds of the ship." Leonardo is speaking here of the ship marked *ba* (at the top). "The ship *dc*," he adds, "does the opposite, and *fe* has a movement midway between the two aforesaid." If you sliced through a modern racing yacht two or three feet below the waterline, you would see that its shape quite closely resembles ship *ba*.

Leonardo thought it natural to study fish as a guide to boat design, just as he studied birds before sketching many of his designs for flying machines. Modern designers, however, were making mistakes in airplane shape long after streamlining had been introduced for boats. Leonardo's method followed his belief that nature is always the best designer.

Quite recently, the study of fish has been carried one step further with ship's speed in mind. A German scientist, Dr. Max O. Kramer, watching porpoises moving rapidly through the water, noticed that the water they pushed aside as they swam had less "revolutions," as Leonardo said, or turbulence, as we call it, than are usual with a moving ship. He decided to study the matter, and discovered that porpoises have a special kind of flexible skin, which explains what he noticed. As a result, he has experimented with copying this effect for the outer hull of a ship. Another line of experiment, however, has left the water to the naturally streamlined fish; recent designs enable the ship's hull to lift out of the water as it moves along on ski-like runners. This kind of boat, the hydrofoil, skims over the water's surface at speeds approaching those of an automobile.

PADDLE-WHEEL BOAT NEEDED NO OARS to propel it. Leonardo's designs, made about three hundred years before Fulton's first paddle-wheel steamboat appeared, show various ways of making the paddle wheels turn. In the one shown here, the boatman grasps the horizontal bar inside the boat and turns it with almost the same motion as rowing. The bar connects directly with the wheels, and revolves them. A more complicated plan called for gear connections between the wheels and a pair of treadles that moved up and down alternately. The gear system changed the up-and-down motion of the treadle to rotary motion for the wheels.

Leonardo's treadle arrangement for turning the paddle wheels was original, but the paddle wheel itself had been thought of quite some time before. A certain Roman, whose name is not known, wrote a little book, around A.D. 375, in which he suggested a paddle-wheel boat as an improvement for the Roman navy. This one worked with two winches aboard, each turned by three oxen, and it had three pairs of paddle wheels. Nobody paid much attention to the book at the time, and the boat was not built. But in 1818, about ten years after Fulton launched the ship he unromantically called *The Steamboat*, a man in the English town of Yarmouth built a boat such as the unknown Roman had described. Not six oxen but four horses turned the winches on this boat, and it traveled at six miles an hour. Leonardo almost certainly saw the Roman book with the paddle-wheel design in it, as copies of it were available in Italy during his lifetime.

Oddly enough, Robert Fulton, who made the paddle-wheel boat a going concern, started his career as a painter of miniatures. He left America as a young man to go to England for study with the famous artist Benjamin West, then lost interest in art and took up engineering. When he had been back in the United States for some time, he came to its aid by building a floating fort to defend New York harbor during the War of 1812.

LEONARDO FORESAW TRAFFIC JAMS when he designed the two-level bridge in the center of this page of drawings. He noted that "this bridge will never collapse if the main supports are strong and well put together." Pedestrians were to cross on the upper level, while the lower level accommodated carts and carriages. Many bridges now have two levels, but because walking is almost obsolete in the machine age, both levels are used by trucks and cars.

Leonardo's design for this truss bridge preceded the general use of strut construction for bridge building. He understood that joining the wooden beams into triangular sections would provide the strongest support for the bridge, because a triangle, more than a square or any other figure with straight sides, resists being bent out of shape.

About three hundred years after this sketch was made, Tom Paine, the fiery pamphleteer of the American Revolution, astonished everybody by designing a truss bridge made of cast iron. People couldn't understand how a bridge supported only at the ends could hold up under the weight of traffic. A model of the bridge was exhibited in Benjamin Franklin's Philadelphia garden, where it created a sensation, but the difficulties of having the bridge accepted for construction across a river in New Jersey caused Paine to return to his native England. The English eventually built the bridge, but Paine meanwhile became involved in English and French politics; he fled from England to France, where he was first welcomed and later jailed during the events following the French Revolution. The story goes that the door of his cell was marked with chalk one day to show that he was on the list of those to be executed, but Paine escaped guillotining because the cell door happened to be open at the time, and the chalk mark swung to the inside when the door was closed. Besides the bridge, Paine invented several other things, including a smokeless candle and a machine for planing wood.

Below the two-level bridge Leonardo showed a plan for rapid communication in wartime. The idea was to build a house every mile, connecting the houses with a long tunnel. A guard inside each house kept his eye out to watch for news and his ear ready to hear somebody else's news shouted through the tunnel. Leonardo estimated that if anything worthy of repeating happened, it would take about fifteen minutes to send the news one hundred miles by shouting through the tunnel from house to house. His system, though ingenious, did not equal Napoleon's network of semaphore signals placed all over Europe. Signalmen on hilltops could and did transmit news across the Continent at a rate at least as fast as Leonardo imagined.

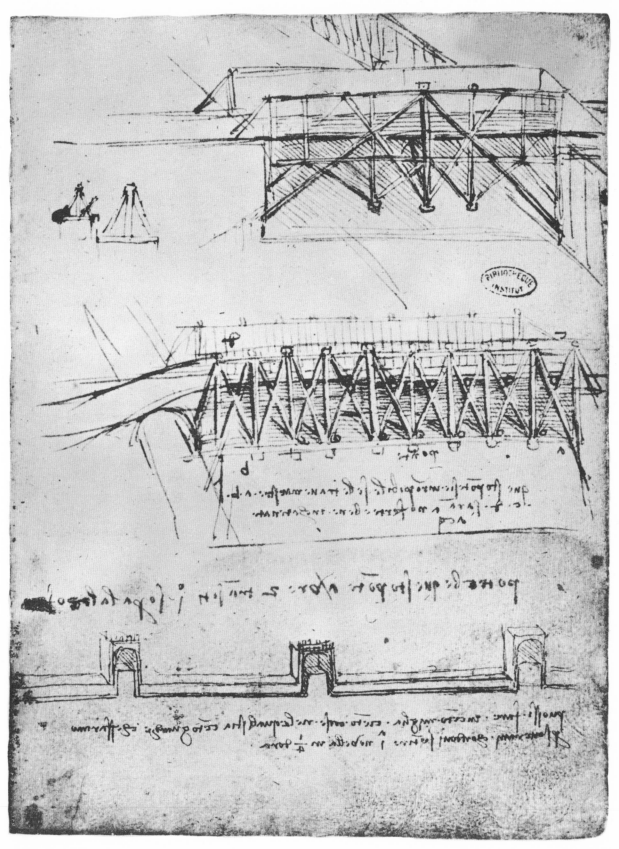

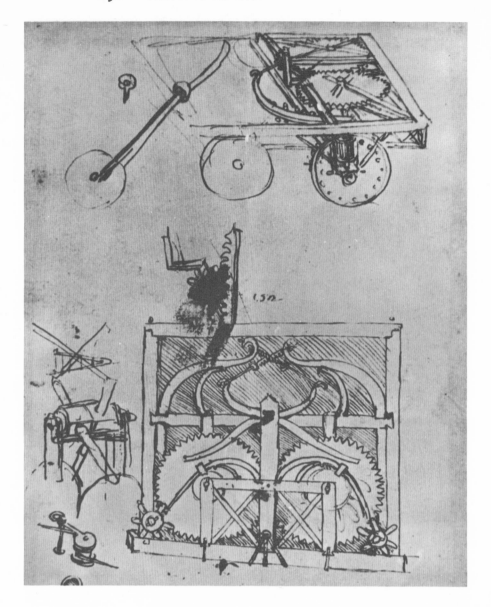

LEONARDO'S HORSELESS WAGON, designed four hundred years before the modern horseless carriage hit the road, moved by power
from the alternate release of twin springs. While a spring on one
side unwound itself, the driver turned a crank handle to rewind the
other. Each spring connected with the wheels by means of a pulley
system, and the car was steered by a long shaft like the steering rod
on a scooter, except that Leonardo put his steering rod at the back
of the wagon. The two parallel wheels are in front, followed by
two single wheels lined up under the wagon's center. Toy cars wound
with a key work on springs such as Leonardo had in mind, but as
they have only one spring instead of two, the car soon stops until
the key is wound again.

Leonardo thought out a transmission system for wagon wheels to turn at different speeds when the wagon rounds a curve, and he probably intended using it on this automatic wagon (see section on Power for details).

If Leonardo had lived in Holland, where windmills were such an important source of power, he might have thought of the wind carriage, which had windmill arms on top. A two-masted carriage of this type was reportedly running in Holland in the year 1600, going twenty miles an hour with twenty-eight people aboard! And the Chinese had used the idea a thousand years earlier.

Less than a century after the Dutch wind carriage sailed along the roads, a model steam carriage was built, and by 1769 a Frenchman had designed a steam-powered tricycle that made a successful trial run at more than two miles an hour, only a little slower than walking. It carried four passengers and ran for twenty minutes. Though not as efficient as the wind carriage, this tricycle was closer to the modern automobile because, like Leonardo's wagon, it carried its own power system rather than depending on the outside force of wind. Service stations were first suggested by an Englishman who patented a car designed to run by a compressed-air engine. The year was 1799.

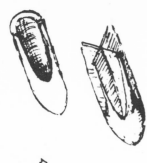

WAR

"He who does not control his impulse classes himself with beasts."

Sometimes men of the same country fight one another; more often country fights country. The fighting may be a mere border skirmish or it may involve the major powers of the world, but there seems never to be a time when everyone in the world lays aside his weapons and decides to settle things another way. The usual pattern of war is for each side to talk about "defense," calling the other side an "aggressor," and for large countries to crash into smaller countries, claiming they have come to protect the people who live there. While a few madmen like Genghis Khan and Adolf Hitler openly believe in murder as a solution to problems, most people, from private individuals to heads of government, recognize war as the worst plague of the human race. Meanwhile, we continue inventing more deadly weapons.

World War I killed about 8,500,000 people. By World War II, the means of killing had been so improved that the deaths doubled. Our newest weapon of the time, the atomic bomb, conclusively proved its efficiency: only two such bombs were needed to kill more than 150,000 Japanese. There are people who suggest using this weapon again as a means of winning local wars, but in the opinion of the United Nations' chief executive, anyone who makes such a suggestion is "out of his mind."

Leonardo would undoubtedly have agreed with the UN Secretary General, but he might also have invented the atomic bomb, had he lived in the twentieth century. He hated war and killing, whether of men or animals, but he spent a great deal of time thinking of new ways for people to kill one another. Leonardo's most famous letter, addressed to the Duke of Milan, dealt with his ideas for all sorts of destructive devices, and offered his services as a military engineer. Not only the Duke of Milan but Cesare Borgia himself employed Leonardo's talents for military purposes. Borgia goes down in history as a man whose "fine Italian hand" was always ready for a tricky scheme or an equally tricky case of poisoning or stabbing.

War in the fifteenth century had little resemblance to twentieth-century warfare. Armies besieged fortresses or fought on open battlefields. Transportation was by horse or on foot, and the archer took his place with the gunner. Because the invention of gunpowder and guns was changing the strategy of war and the design of fortresses, the men on foot were becoming more important than the men on horses, but these changes had not yet taken full effect. In 1492, the year of Columbus' great voyage, the Spanish city of Granada became the first place ever taken by artillery. Leonardo saw the changes coming, and, as a military designer, often thought in terms of the future war.

For every aspect of warfare, he considered the problems of both offense and defense. He thought of practical ways to improve cannon design and construction, and he studied the theory of projectiles, recognizing that a round cannon ball "strikes more air and finds more resistance," while a bomb shaped like our modern missiles "enters upon the air edgewise . . . and more rapidly moves through it." One sketch for such a bomb not only includes tail fins but a method of exploding the bomb when it hits the target; it might be intended for modern warfare. Shrapnel was also on Leonardo's list, and he even invented a gun that propelled the cannon ball by the force of a steam jet.

Just as he designed weapons to attack a fortress, Leonardo designed fortresses to resist the attack, and his ideas on this subject were equally modern. A round fortress, mostly underground, would be much harder to overcome, he believed, than a fortress with flat walls and a large exposed surface as a target; the fortress plans of our times were developed on the same theory. Leonardo also considered temporary field fortifications, a revival of the long-forgotten Roman idea. His notes discuss how to scale a wall and how to stop it being scaled, how to make a military bridge and how to destroy it, how to make underground mine shafts for invading a fortress, and how to detect them. To detect mine-shaft digging, he suggested, you placed a pair of dice on top of a musical drum and set the drum over the spot where you suspected the enemy might be cutting an underground passage. As soon as work began underground, the vibrations caused by the blows of the pickax would make the dice jump around on the drum and you would outwit the enemy.

Fifteenth-century naval strategy called for warships to be galleys rowed by oarsmen, as opposed to the sailing ships of commerce. For victory at sea, Leonardo recommended various methods of ramming an enemy ship, above the waterline or below it. One of his wilder notions was a tool to attach the ship to the bottom of the sea, so that when the enemy tried to move the ship, it would remain anchored. He invented several devices for divers, ranging from a breathing tube like a snorkel (see section on Water for details) to a diving suit that enclosed the man completely; all were for military use. Possibly, he had ideas about a submarine, but we'll never know; he said only, "How and why I do not describe my method for remaining underwater for as long a time as I can remain without food; and this I do not publish or divulge on account of the evil nature of men who would practice assassination at the bottom of the seas. . . ." Maybe Leonardo wouldn't have "divulged" the atomic bomb either. ✛

THREE WAYS TO DESIGN A MACHINE GUN for multiple firing power were considered in this sketch. The one at the top had three rows of twelve barrels each arranged on a large triangular mount. By turning the triangle to place a different face on top, a new row of guns was made available. As Leonardo conceived the idea, one row would be shooting, one row would be loading, and the third would be cooling after use.

Surprising as it may seem, the principle of combining many barrels into one weapon had been fairly well established in fifteenth-century warfare. The machine gun's ancestor was the ribaudequin, a weapon that mounted many pikes together for shooting in quick succession or all at once. Though firearms naturally changed the manner of fighting, their efficiency at first left a good deal to be desired. A bow could be loaded and shot twelve times as fast as a gun; as late as the sixteenth century, a gun took so long to load that it could fire only one shot every two minutes. Nor were its range and accuracy dependable, mostly because nobody could tell exactly how much gunpowder to use. Too much led to a disastrous explosion that might demolish the gunner (the fine old phrase "hoist by your own petard" derived from the danger of being blown up this way by your own petard, or bomb) and too little led to a useless fizzle. As if these disadvantages weren't enough, guns also went against the principles of the Age of Chivalry: a chivalrous soldier didn't mind cutting up his enemy with a sword, but thought it unsporting to shoot him from a distance!

Machine guns in the modern sense first saw action toward the end of the American Civil War, when Richard J. Gatling's gun came into use. Like an oversized revolver, it had one barrel with a drum at the end divided into chambers; these were moved into shooting position by turning a crank. Later models used the energy released by the burning gunpowder to feed, load, and lock the gun, fire the next round, and empty the used cartridge case. The newest machine-gun design, however, has returned to Leonardo's principle of many barrels. One of these guns, run by an outside motor, has six barrels and can fire more than 1,500 rounds of ammunition a minute.

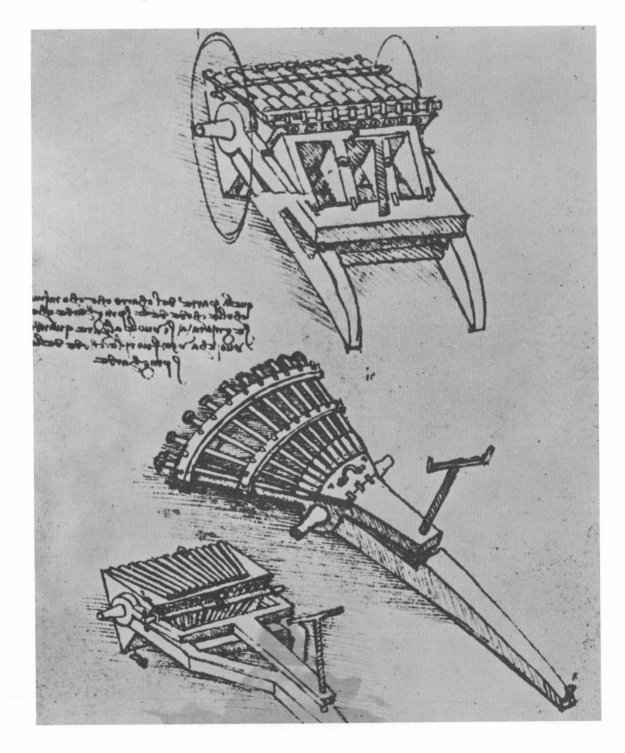

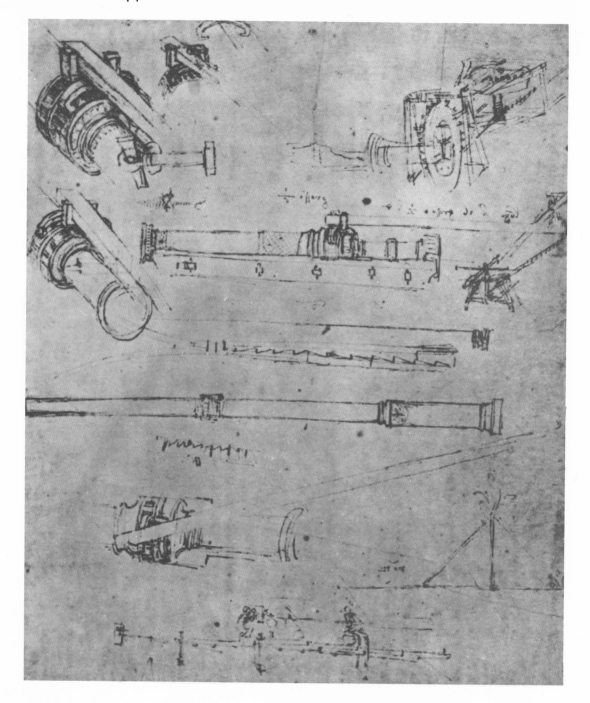

WHEEL-LOCK CLOSURE FOR A BREECH-LOADING CANNON, sketched in the upper left corner of this drawing, gave the breech end of the cannon more strength than the other closure methods in use at the time. In the open position, the cannon ball could be lifted into the cannon and the powder placed in the powder chamber that formed part of the device itself. Then the wheel was turned by a crank handle to screw the closure firmly into place, and the heavy frame around it offered extra protection. The usual fifteenth-century method called for a sort of cylindrical cage extension welded to the cannon barrel's breech end, and a separate powder chamber to be lowered to the cage. This chamber was, in effect, an iron box, open at the end leading into the barrel. Such a flimsy arrangement risked being blown off by recoil every time the gunner fired the cannon.

Shortly before Leonardo thought of using a wheel and screw to close a cannon breech, Charles VIII of France invaded Naples, defeating the Italians by means of cannon mounted on wheels and drawn by horses. Previously, oxen had dragged cannon along on carriages resembling large sleds. The French gained a double tactical advantage: just as a wheel is more efficient than a sled runner on rough ground, a horse is for most jobs a more efficient work animal than an ox.

The American Army has never used a wheel-lock method for closing the breech of a cannon; possibly because it takes too much time to screw the closure into place, a device worked on hinges was preferred. And one must speak of the cannon in the past tense, as missiles have made it an obsolete weapon. The navy, however, uses a wheel-lock arrangement similar in principle to Leonardo's for closing the hatches of its submarines to make them watertight.

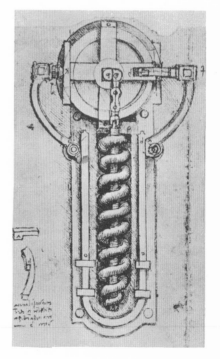

IT'S NOT A CIGARETTE LIGHTER, but this gadget to light the powder in a cannon works on the same principle and is about the same size. The arm on the left holds the flint next to the wheel rim. The gunner turns the keylike handle at the center, thus tightening the large spring below and locking the wheel with the arm on the right. He then presses down on the right arm, suddenly releasing the spring to whirl the wheel sharply against the flint and strike a spark.

The explosive charge in modern artillery pieces is ignited by a very different method. Next to the charge that propels the bullet is a small quantity of a special explosive highly sensitive to shock. When the gunner pulls the trigger, he automatically moves a mechanism that jars this explosive so that it ignites, transmitting the fire to the other charge and sending off the projectile. This system dates from the American Civil War period. Before that, the flintlock gun automatically touched off the charge, when the trigger was pulled, by a device that did the same thing as Leonardo's lighter. Unlike Leonardo's gadget, the flintlock was built into the gun.

"THE STEAM GUN IS A MACHINE made of fine copper . . . and it throws small iron balls with great noise and fury." As the picture and the model show, the part of the barrel nearest the breech is surrounded by a charcoal fire and acts as a powder chamber. Leonardo explains that when this section of the barrel has been thoroughly heated by the fire, the gunner must turn the horizontal screw at the very top of the machine. Tightening this screw will loosen the vertical screw just below, which is in the middle of a chamber of water heated by the fire at the bottom. When the vertical screw is loosened, says Leonardo, it "uncorks" the board that serves as the floor of the water chamber, thus releasing the very hot water with a rush to fall into the heated part of the gun barrel. At that moment, the water "will instantly become changed into so much steam that it will seem marvelous, and especially when one sees its fury and hears its roar." The sudden blast of steam propels the cannon ball.

Leonardo claimed that the steam gun had shot a 60-pound ball more than two-thirds of a mile. Certainly, the idea of using steam as a source of power was most original at the time. About 250 years later, the idea was used again by an Englishman named James Perkins who patented a steam rocket having some of the same features as Leonardo's steam gun. The main body of the rocket resembled a food can with a small hole in the bottom, plugged with metal of low melting point. A nose cone was attached to the top. The can was partially filled with water and placed in a fire. In due time, the water turned to steam and the plug melted, leaving the hole open for steam to escape. As the steam rushed out of the hole, the rocket rose. The gadget worked, but nobody now knows what Perkins had in mind for its use. Soon after this puzzling invention was recorded, another Englishman patented a steam horse, on which, he said, "one may ride in one hour from Paris to St. Petersburg [Russia]"; unfortunately, no picture of the steam horse survives.

On more solid ground, the modern pile driver employs Leonardo's idea of steam as the driving force. Steam made in a boiler provides the power to raise the hammer between blows and allow it to fall, and also to work the crane that sets the pile in place before it is driven into the ground. In construction, the term "pile" describes whatever will be used to make a building foundation; it is often a hollow steel cylinder, first driven into the ground, then filled with concrete. Leonardo designed a pile driver, but its hammer was pulled up by a winch; a reliable steam pressure could not have been produced in Leonardo's time.

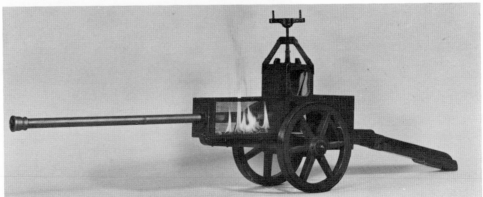

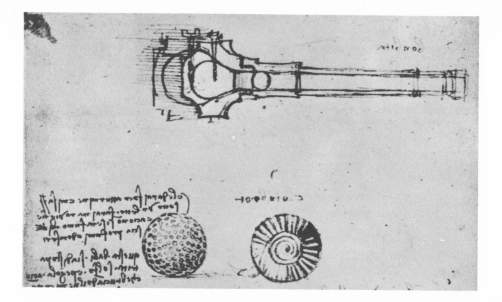

"THIS IS THE MOST DEADLY WEAPON THAT EXISTS," Leonardo said of shrapnel, and he invented several kinds. The one shown here, in the round and in cross section, consists of sticks, or "canes," as Leonardo describes them, projecting in every direction from a central core and protruding slightly from the surface of the shrapnel ball. The whole ball is constructed to be highly inflammable; a soldier ignites the ends of the canes on the ball's surface just before he shoots the ball from a catapult. Then, Leonardo explains, "As the ball reaches the ground, the canes which are bound at the top with ignited linen cloth are driven into it, thus igniting the powder which surrounds a piece of tow that has been soaked in turpentine," and the whole ball bursts and scatters its flaming shreds. The drawing above the shrapnel shows a view of Leonardo's wheel-lock closure for a breech-loading cannon, explained elsewhere in this section.

Another of his shrapnel devices substituted small balls for the canes inside the shell, and Leonardo predicted that when the shell burst, it would scatter the smaller balls, "which catch fire in such time as is needed to say an Ave Maria." He also thought of filling his shrapnel balls with an evil-smelling mixture so strong that he advised care in its use, because, if it landed in the wrong place, "it would be just as harmful to you as to your enemies," and "there is no remedy to prevent its pestilential effect."

Leonardo also had a recipe for gunpowder, very close to a modern formula with one exception: in addition to the charcoal, sulfur, and saltpeter that he prescribed, he recommended the use of good brandy to moisten it!

IN PRINCIPLE, MORTARS HAVEN'T CHANGED MUCH since Leonardo drew this picture of two mortars in action, shooting fireballs. By the fifteenth century, the mortar was a standard weapon, often preferred to the cannon because it weighed less and could be fired more easily. Its short-barrel design made it useful for sending projectiles high into the air over the wall of a fortification.

The mortar evolved from an old weapon called the trebuchet, a long pole balanced horizontally on two upright poles that formed a line pointing to the target. One end of the horizontal pole projected much farther than the other; therefore, when the short end was pulled down it acted like a lever, and sent the long end up a much greater distance. By loading the long end with a rock and pulling down the short end suddenly, the rock could be made to sail over the top of a high wall.

Shortly after Leonardo's time, the Russians built a mortar that could fire a stone missile weighing a ton. It was called the Great Mortar of Moscow; strangely enough, it was something like Little David, an American mortar built during World War II and capable of firing a missile of almost two tons. Little David was designed to attack underground forts and industrial centers, but its weight and handling difficulties made it quite unpopular. The typical World War II mortar weighed about 43 pounds and had a range of 200 yards to a little over a mile. Like the mortars Leonardo drew, it did a front-line job, hurling shells into enemy lines over the tops of hills. And, like the earlier mortars too, it was muzzle-loaded.

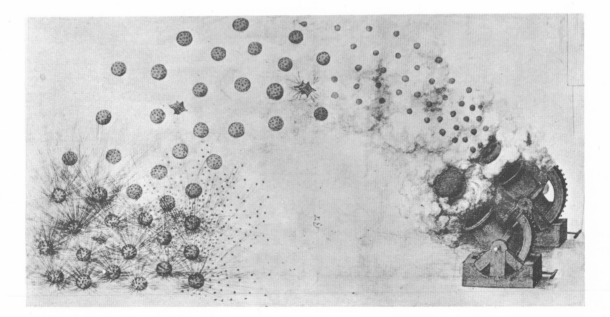

A LEFTOVER BOMB FROM WORLD WAR II? No, this is the fifteenth-century version of a directional-fin projectile. The fins near the tail help keep the bomb on course, while the two bent rods near the nose are brought violently against the body to ignite the powder inside when the bomb hits its target. This device is a forerunner of the modern percussion cap, which serves the same purpose.

Looking at the completely modern shape and concept of this bomb, you may be startled to know that it was meant to be shot from a large bow! Bombs or bullets shaped like this one were not practical for guns until a method of rifling the inside of a gun barrel had been developed. Rifling means making parallel grooves down the length of the barrel; the grooves are somewhat spiraled so that they give the projectile a spin as it leaves the barrel. The spinning motion, and the fins on this bomb, makes the projectile less subject to being blown off course by the wind. Leonardo thought of rifling guns for this purpose, but it wasn't done until much later. He wisely realized that an old-fashioned bow would be more effective than a crude gun for shooting his explosive bomb.

"I HAVE PLANS FOR BRIDGES," Leonardo wrote to the Duke of Milan in a letter stating his qualifications as a military engineer. He described the bridges as "very light and strong, and suitable for carrying very easily," and he stated that they would be useful "to pursue and at times defeat the enemy."

The three bridges shown here can be swung to one side of the stream after soldiers cross them, leaving the enemy stranded on the other side. At the top, Leonardo drew a rope bridge that rests on piers set in the stream, thus gaining enough strength to support the weight of traffic across it; as the piers must remain in a fixed position, the bridge structure moves off them when it is swung. The arched bridge below, constructed on the cantilever principle, is made of wood and is swung by a winch at the right that winds up the rope passing over the bridge tower and pulls the bridge to one side. Look closely and you can see a man on horseback crossing the bridge. At the bottom is a pontoon bridge resting on barges, and Leonardo has a bit of advice about it: "Make it so that in the movement of the bridge the length of the barges will always find itself in line with the current, when the movement will be as much easier as the barges receive less percussion from the water."

Pontoon bridges have been used in military campaigns since at least 500 B.C. by the Greeks and Persians, and they were still in use during World War II, when the Allies used a bridge of this type to cross the Rhine. When "all Gaul" was "divided into three parts," Caesar had set a precedent for crossing the Rhine; his bridge, built around 55 B.C., was of a more permanent nature, consisting of trestles that rested on piles. Like the Allies, he built it to defeat the Germans, and succeeded.

Leonardo's design for an arched swing bridge does not seem to have been put into use either by him or by others. Swing bridges usually move around a pivot in the middle of the stream, while lift bridges may be raised in one piece from one end, in two pieces from both ends, or lifted straight up without tilting.

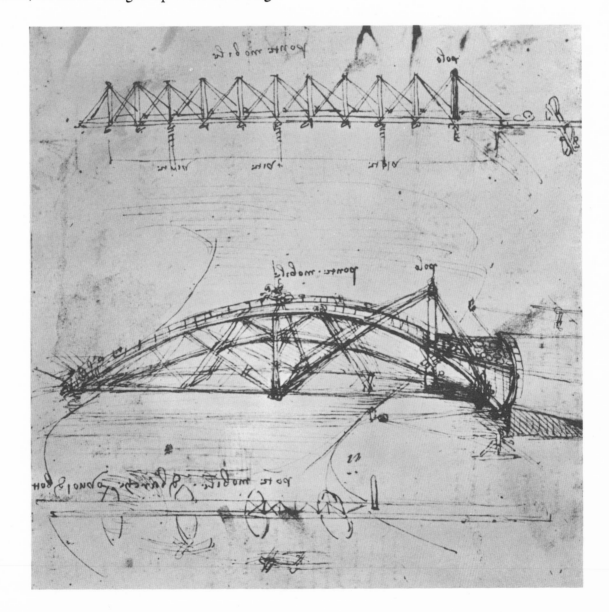

ARMORED TANK TO PENETRATE ENEMY LINES was constructed of heavy wooden beams set close together. It carried light breech-loading cannon that could be loaded inside the tank and fired through the gap between the lower part of the vehicle and its pointed roof. This gap also let in enough light so that the gunners could see what they were doing. The sketch of the tank upside down shows that the wheels were connected in pairs by cage gears and cranks that could be turned by men inside the tank. At the top of his drawing Leonardo has sketched a type of military machine used by the ancient Persians and Britons; this chariot, propelled by a man on horseback, was equipped with projecting scythe blades that revolved as the chariot moved forward to mow down the enemy.

In principle, the idea of the tank might be said to have begun with the famous elephants Hannibal marched through the Alps when he tried to capture Rome in the third century B.C. Leonardo was one of several Renaissance military designers who thought of using an armored vehicle, but the tank never became an important weapon until World War I, when it was developed and brought into use mostly because of the enthusiasm of Sir Winston Churchill. As First Lord of the Admiralty in 1914, Churchill believed an armored car would effectively protect advance air bases, and Sir Ernest Swinton developed such a car, using the American caterpillar farm tractor as his model. When the British War Office showed little interest in the project, Churchill created a special commission to continue it.

Because the tank came into being under navy sponsorship, it was originally known as a landship, and naval terms like "hull," "deck," "hatch," and "turret" still describe its parts. It got the name "tank" in military dispatches to keep its identity secret.

THE DOUBLE-HULLED SHIP COULD STILL FLOAT if the outer hull suffered damage. Leonardo suggested this construction for ships "for their safety in time of war," but he did not say exactly how the ship should be built.

Modern battleships, aircraft carriers, and some large passenger ships have double-hull construction for safety. Sometimes it saves the ship from sinking, but at other times the force of impact due to accident or attack may be strong enough to penetrate both hulls. A double hull didn't save the Italian liner *Andrea Doria* when she collided with the *Stockholm* in a fog off Nantucket some years ago.

The other drawing in this picture shows what Leonardo called "a mysterious vessel for sinking enemy ships." Some people have believed that he was thinking of a submarine, but if so, he did not explain how he would move it underwater or bring it to the surface. It may surprise you to know, though, that in 1620, the same year the *Mayflower* lumbered across the Atlantic, C. J. Drebbel, a Dutchman living in England, built a submarine that cruised at the bottom of the Thames River. This boat, entirely covered with leather, was rowed by twelve men using oars that went through watertight leather seals on the hull. The air supply was provided for on the snorkel principle. Leonardo's sketch looks nothing like this boat, of course, and we'll never know how his mysterious vessel was to accomplish its dark purpose.

A DIVER WOULD DISABLE ENEMY SHIPS by getting under them in a harbor and prying apart planks of the hulls to cause leaks. The larger sketch shows how to do this. Leonardo describes the suit the diver must order to be made for the job: "A breastplate of armor, hood, jacket and stockings, and a small wineskin attached for urinating . . . another wineskin to hold air for breathing, with a semicircle of iron to keep it away from the chest. . . . A mask with glass windows, but the weight must be light enough so that you can raise it as you swim. . . . Bring with you a knife that cuts well so that you will not be caught in a net." Leonardo also refers to bags of sand to be used as ballast for sinking, and other bags to be inflated with air for rising to the surface, but doesn't mention how the inflating works.

It is possible that Leonardo may have been asked by the rulers of Venice to figure out how to sink Turkish ships then in Venice's harbor, and that the job may have reached the planning stage. "Get a simple-minded young man to sew it up at home," says Leonardo, so that nobody will guess what the diving suit is for; he also speaks of a secret document to be drawn up that will guarantee proper payment for the risk. And, he adds at the end, "Bring a horn to signal the success or failure of your effort." A failure might have been hard to signal.

The most unusual feature of this diving suit is its self-contained air supply in the "wineskin to hold air for breathing." It wouldn't work for very long, but the diver was supposed to do his work in a harbor, near the shore, and stay down only a short while in rather shallow water. Modern diving suits of the type Leonardo described have an air line to the surface, but skindivers carry air tanks on their backs, following his idea of the self-contained supply. The tank may contain one of several breathing mixtures. With a mixture of oxygen and helium, divers can go down almost 400 feet. With a compressed-air mixture, a diver has to be more careful because the nitrogen in the air starts making him sleepy as he goes deeper: at 130 feet deep, he feels as if he had sipped a strong cocktail, and by 200 feet down he will feel as if he had drunk several. Divers call this danger the Law of Martini.

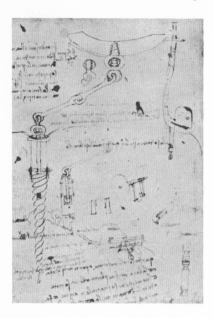

THIS UNDERSEA ANCHOR FOR THE ENEMY used a drill to make a hole in the sea bottom. The diver was to go down secretly and fix the drill in the bottom, then somehow attach the other end of the apparatus to the hull of the enemy ship so that it couldn't move. Here Leonardo seems to be showing how the drill hangs from a floating buoy, to which the diver also secures his breathing tube, but it is not clear how the diver should attach the drill handle to the hull after the bit is fixed in the sea bottom. He gives some other interesting details, however: "In order to turn this screw, use a pair of slippers with heels or hooks so that the foot may stand firm," presumably on the bottom, and, he adds, go in a wineskin boat, with a valve to let water in so that you can sink the boat and keep it near you while you work underwater.

The idea of secret underwater mischief is of course the whole principle of submarine warfare, which first turned up in the American Revolution. A man named David Bushnell built a small submarine moved by a hand crank that turned the propeller. It looked like an egg with a conning tower and had special tanks to flood or empty for sinking or surfacing the boat. Unfortunately, Bushnell had not solved the air-supply problem, so he could stay down for only a very short time. Nevertheless he convinced General Washington that he could blow up the British ships in New York harbor. One night in 1776, Bushnell set out to try a plan that Leonardo might have invented. He proposed to approach a ship in his submarine, attach a drill bit to its hull, and release a torpedo that would be fastened to the drill to direct it to the target. In the time it would take the torpedo to go off, the submarine could escape to safety. The submarine also had a special crank to work the drill. Bushnell and his sub got as far as a British hull, only to find that the drill wouldn't penetrate the copper sheathing. But he gave the British a good scare when they discovered what he was up to.

THE CIRCULAR FORTRESS WAS A NEW IDEA of Leonardo's in which alternating rings of water and fortifications protected the stronghold at the center. Leonardo recognized that a round fortress would be desirable because the receding line of a circle offers less surface than a flat wall to enemy fire. A round wall also has more strength against bombardment. He combined strength of design with two other original features. First, he planned as much as possible of the fortress to be underground or underwater, leaving the minimum exposed

surface as a target. Second, he placed outworks at four points around
his circle, so that the defenders could set up crossfire in any direction
necessary.

In some of these respects, Leonardo's fortress designs were so
modern in concept that they have been compared with the famous
Maginot Line. Leonardo's fortress could probably have withstood
the fifteenth-century weapons used against it, but the Maginot Line,
as the French learned at such cost, was inadequate against World
War II strategy and arms. Even if it had been complete when the
Nazis attacked, they still could have dive-bombed it from above and
flown around the end of it, exactly as they did. The Maginot Line
was designed on the basis of World War I, a war less mobile than
World War II. In other words, it was one war behind the new
achievements in destruction. Since the invention of the atomic bomb,
no fortress would be of any use except in a local war, when both
sides agree to be "gentlemen" and refrain from dropping it. The
only known impenetrable defense against atomic attack is peace.

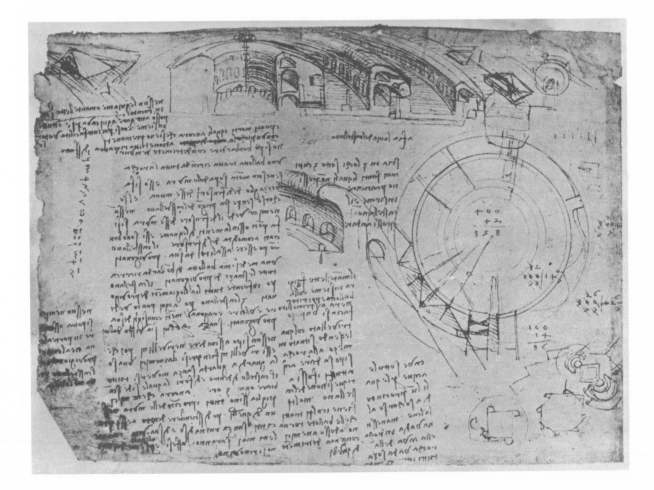

WATER

"Water of itself does not move unless it descends."

As surely as a magnet attracts steel filings, water attracts civilization. The Fertile Crescent, area of the oldest known civilization, was fertile because it lay between the Tigris and the Euphrates rivers, which supplied water for irrigation. Its other name, Mesopotamia, means "between rivers." Many ancient civilizations surrounded a large body of water, the Mediterranean Sea; later, a still larger stretch of water, the Atlantic Ocean, led to the settlement of America, where the most important cities were built along the great coastline facing two oceans and the Gulf of Mexico, or bordering one of the Great Lakes or inland rivers. Water is so necessary to modern life that its use in this country amounts, on the average, to about 150 gallons a day for each one of us.

Civilization and water go together, first because we need to drink water for survival, and also because it keeps us clean, moistens the land for growing crops, provides power for turning machines, and forms a highroad for commerce. When water is harnessed, it becomes nature's most beneficial force; out of control, it acts as an unconquerable enemy, sweeping over the land and leaving a wake of destruction behind it.

Water fascinated Leonardo, who called it the "driver of nature." In Italy he could see water in all its aspects, from the fast-moving mountain brook to the sea it reaches after first becoming a river; or the many tiny streams trickling slowly over a plain to become a swamp. River currents and eddies, ocean tides, and the way water wears down soil and hard rock all concerned him, and he had a special interest in the falling water that turned water wheels, the key to power-driven machinery. The problems of swimmers interested him too, and, as usual, he invented devices for them that look up to date.

Watching the flowing rivers, Leonardo noticed that river water runs faster near the surface where it touches the light air than near the bottom where it must overcome the resistance of the heavier earth. Water also runs faster, he observed, in a straight stream or pipe than in one with bends, and he understood that the surface of the ocean or a lake may be disturbed by the wind while the bottom remains still. He planned to write a book about water with fifteen chapters on "the nature of the depths," "the surface of water," "machines turned by water," "how to make the water ascend," and many other subjects. Though he never wrote the book, he left numerous notes about water and drew superb sketches showing details of its motion.

Many of his observations were made for practical purposes. At Milan, he took charge of water engineering, or hydraulics, and supervised the building of several canal connections in the region. Leonardo's sketches show new ideas about machinery for canal digging and especially about lock-gate design. Another of his studies dealt with the angle at which water leaves small spouts at different levels of a tank. Because the water at the bottom of the tank is under more pressure than the water near the top, the water jet from the lower spout will form a different arc than the top one; Leonardo noted that this information could be used to judge the depth of the water in a reservoir.

Of "machines turned by water" Leonardo had several, including a hydraulic screw that worked on a principle similar to that of the modern water turbine (see the section on Power for details). And applying his knowledge of "how to make the water ascend," he installed a water-supply pump for the Milan castle. In addition, he designed what we now call an air-lift pump, which raises water by the upward motion of air bubbles that make it lighter, and a centrifugal pump, intended for use in swamp drainage. His most ambitious hydraulics project aimed at diverting the course of the river Arno, so as to give Florence a water route to the sea, but neither sufficient money nor equipment was available to carry out the plan.

Leonardo understood the process of water evaporating from the sea and returning to earth as rain, then flowing through streams and rivers to the sea again. He became so engrossed in comparing the water cycle with the circulation of blood in the human body that he blinded himself to the facts about blood circulation when he made anatomical dissections. Instead, he decided that a man has in him "a pool of blood" that rises and falls like the ocean tides when he breathes.

But for Leonardo, water meant much more than a vital substance to be studied and used in a practical way. The twisting shapes of moving water and its great power of destruction took such a hold on his mind that he predicted a disastrous deluge would destroy the world, and he drew a series of magnificently ominous pictures to show how it would happen. ✠

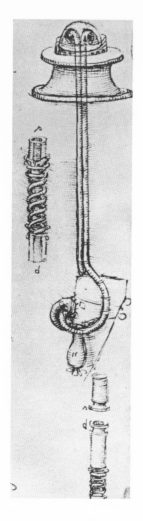

THIS BREATHING TUBE HAD TWIN PIPES for inhaling and exhaling; these connected with a floating air-supply dome on the water's surface. Leonardo arranged the mouthpiece so that the diver's mouth would be connected alternately with each pipe as the diver breathed in and out. Although Leonardo was aware of the problem of underwater breathing through a long tube, due to increasing water pressure, he apparently did not solve it. Breathing tubes like his will work to a depth of about two feet; beyond that, the pressure of the water prevents the diver from inhaling because his lungs aren't strong enough to expand against it. Our snorkels are designed for use a foot and a half or less below the surface; the swimmer breathes in and out through one tube which, like Leonardo's, sticks out of the water.

Hundreds of years before anyone thought of diving equipment, divers had taken part in naval battles or hunted for pearls. But the first mention of a breathing tube precedes Leonardo by a long period: the Roman historian Pliny, living in the first century of the Christian era, reported the use of a breathing tube resembling the one in this sketch. Military divers, he said, had been equipped with it. A few hundred years after that, another Roman, named Vegetius, described a similar device. The trouble with Vegetius' tube was that it led to a windowless hood covering the entire head. If the diver succeeded in breathing, he would certainly not succeed in seeing. Leonardo didn't know about Vegetius, but he must nevertheless be regarded as a latecomer in the history of underwater breathing devices.

FROGMEN IN THE FIFTEENTH CENTURY? This webbed glove might easily be mistaken for the modern fins used by professional divers. Wearing gloves like these would increase swimming speed, just as the foot fins do. However, it's useful when swimming to take advantage of the dexterity of the hands, and wet gloves would interfere. Foot fins are therefore preferable; if you make the foot fins larger or stiffer, they will serve the same purpose as supplementing them with webbed gloves, adding to your power and speed.

Leonardo thought of swimming aids mainly for military use. In World War II, British and American frogmen equipped with foot fins worked near the beaches of Normandy before D Day. Just below the level of the low-water line, the Germans had embedded concrete obstacles, whose jagged projections and sometimes explosive charges could destroy opposing ships trying to land. The frogmen's mission was to clear away these obstacles in advance.

"A METHOD OF ESCAPING IN A TEMPEST and shipwreck at sea." The details follow: "Have a coat made of leather, which should have the part over the breast with two layers, a finger's breadth apart; and in the same way it must be double from the waist to the knee; and the leather must be quite airtight. When you have to leap into the sea, blow on the skirt of your coat through the double layers of the breast; and jump into the sea, and allow yourself to be carried by the waves; when you see no shore near, give your attention to the sea you are in, and always keep in your mouth the air tube which leads down into the coat; and if now and again you need to take a breath of fresh air, and the foam prevents you, you may draw a breath of the air within the coat."

The idea of inflating a leather bag for buoyancy began with the Assyrians, who made rafts of this type for crossing streams. Later, soldiers of the Mongol conqueror Genghis Khan traveled with bags that doubled as rafts and suitcases. But the inflatable bag reached its peak of versatility in the hands of a nineteenth-century inventor. Immanuel Nobel, whose son is remembered for dynamite and the Nobel Prize, figured out a gadget that served as a combination knapsack, mattress, life preserver, and pontoon. The same gentleman also invented modern plywood, and wrote a treatise suggesting its many uses, from cradle to coffin.

The breathing tube of Leonardo's life jacket has a modern counterpart. Small airplanes such as those flying from the Peruvian coast into the high Andes carry an air tube for each passenger; as the air gets thinner, passengers may take whiffs of oxygen through the air tubes to prevent a feeling of faintness.

WALKING ON WATER, according to Leonardo's sketch, required large floating shoes and poles like the ones snow-skiers carry. The shoes would have to be made of a very light wood like balsa, buoyant enough to float under the weight of a man; the water-walker would use the poles to propel himself forward. Anyone who looks at this sketch can't fail to think immediately of modern water skis; Leonardo lacked only the power-driven boat to pull the skier along.

Above the water-walker, Leonardo suggests an extraordinary method of raising water by means of fire. He explains: "Put in this vessel a little tow and set it on fire; close the vessel so as to seal it, and you will soon find it filled with water." He reasoned that by sealing the vessel he would cause the fire inside to use up the oxygen, thus creating a vacuum that would draw up the water from the well in the manner of a suction pump. What the water would taste like mixed with ashes didn't seem to trouble Leonardo, who in this case was more interested in theory than in practice.

WATER FOR THE DUKE OF MILAN'S CASTLE was supplied by a pump like the one shown here. The same stream provided the water and turned the water wheel to work the pump. You can't see here how the pump works because the pistons in their cylinders are in "the stream" inside the base, but you can see the piston rods coming out the top of the two main pipes. The piston rods connect with each other through a rectangular frame at the very top of the whole structure, and the frame moves like a seesaw as one piston goes up while the other goes down. An upstroke of either piston lets water into the cylinder through a flap valve at the bottom, and the downstroke forces the water up through the pipe by means of another flap valve at the top of the cylinder. This kind of arrangement is called a force pump and Leonardo's was said to have been 70 feet high. He must have had some method of disconnecting the pump from the water wheel, which turned all the time. Otherwise the castle would have been flooded quite soon.

The first known fire engine, invented by Hero of Alexandria in the second century B.C., was also one of the first force pumps. It had to carry its own water supply, and Hero didn't explain how it got to the fire, but the idea of pumping water to douse flames is still as good as ever. Two thousand years after Hero had his bright idea, New Yorkers rejoiced at the arrival of a good mobile fire engine from London, and named it Hayseed because it looked like a feed

trough for horses. A bucket brigade furiously poured water into the engine's tublike body, while six men just as furiously worked pump handles to force a stream of water through the hose. The result, which dazzled everybody, was a stream of water of about the force produced by a garden hose. Hayseed ushered in the era of christening parties for fire engines, which received names like Old Maid or Man Killer, according to how they looked. A modern fire engine may be less endearing than the old-fashioned kind, but it can pour out great quantities of water at high pressure, thus making up in efficiency what it lacks in charm. Fire-fighting equipment in Leonardo's period consisted of nothing more than buckets; Hero's fire engine had long been forgotten, and the pumping engine had to be invented all over again. The force pump, however, was well known at the time.

WHAT LEONARDO CALLS A "STORK" is the floating valve with the curved, storklike neck in the lower tank of this water-raising system. The hollow box at the end of the stork's neck rises and falls with the water level in the tank and thus opens and closes a valve to the right that regulates the entrance of additional water into the system from an outside source.

When the stork opens the valve to admit more water, this water is forced upward through the riser pipe by its own pressure, much as pressure forces water in an underground main up the pipes of a house. The water follows the pipe as far as the sharp bend, where another valve opens to let it flow into the upper tank. It is the upper tank that supplies the water for use, probably by a household; the lower tank provides a reserve supply. The valve at the pipe bend is opened and closed by the seesawing of the two buckets at the left-hand end of the upper tank. You can hardly see the buckets in the principal picture, but Leonardo has drawn a separate detail of them at the lower left.

When the valve leading into the upper tank is closed, the water rising in the pipe passes by it and doubles back to flow into the lower tank instead. But when the water in the top tank is used, the top tank draws on the bottom tank for a new supply: the dropping level of the stork then opens the valve to let in more water from the source to the riser pipe, thus refilling the top tank.

Leonardo tries to explain the reason for such a complicated plan: "See to it that the top tank always has at least a foot of water covering the intake and outlet valves because, if you let the tank become empty, air would fill the riser pipe." In other words, the reserve tank at the bottom keeps the top tank properly filled until more water from the source is admitted to the system. Some cars have an emergency gas supply that serves a similar purpose, operating the car for long enough to let the driver reach the next gas station. As for the stork, its most familiar modern use is in the kind of toilet flushed from a water tank. Inside the water tank is a rubber ball that floats up and down with the water level and controls a valve by a mechanism equivalent to Leonardo's stork.

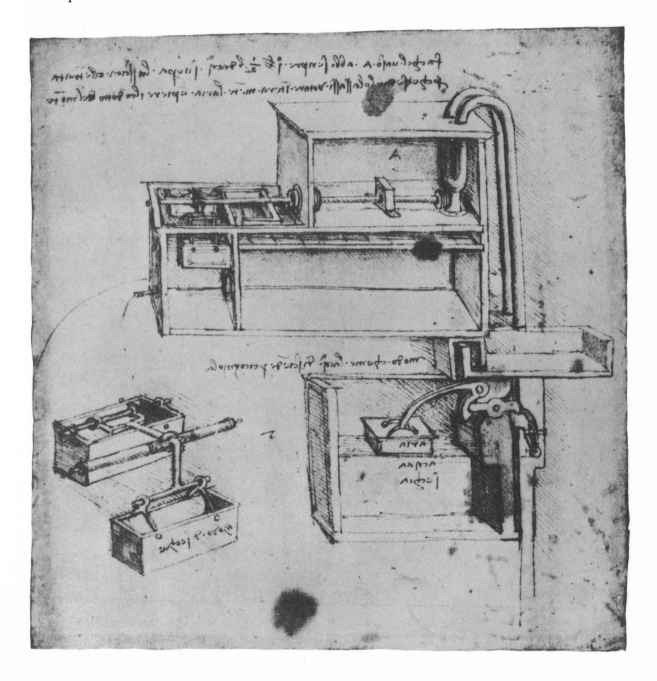

A CONICAL VALVE FLOATS UP AND DOWN as the water level in the pipe rises and falls; by this means it regulates the flow of water through the pipe. If the level of the water rises, the valve closes the top of the chamber, preventing more water from flowing down, but if the water level drops, the valve seals the bottom of the chamber to admit the water from above. The wire running through the valve keeps it moving in a straight line.

The Romans used a valve this shape, but without guide wires, to regulate the rate of water flow into a water clock. The valve floated up and down in the same manner to ensure an even flow in and out of the clock reservoir: like an unwinding coil spring, a water reservoir empties more slowly as the water level drops, because pressure drops too, but the water flow has to be at a steady rate for the water clock to keep accurate time.

We use cone valves now for many purposes. In automobile-engine cylinders, for example, they regulate the fuel intake and exhaust. Made with modern machine tools, the cone valve has the advantage of a leakproof fit because of its shape, but it must have been very difficult to make with fifteenth-century equipment.

"THE HAND TURNING IN A CIRCULAR MOVEMENT in a vessel half full of water," Leonardo explained, "causes an incidental turning [of the water] that exposes the bottom of this vessel to the air." As the right-hand diagram illustrates, the whirling water takes the form of an inverted cone that rises above the top of the vessel and spills over the sides. Leonardo saw this action of whirling water as a possible key to the problem of swamp drainage, and he invented a centrifugal pump he hoped to use for clearing swamps at the edge of the sea.

His several drawings here are based on the assumption that the swamp lies at sea level but is not so deep as the adjoining sea. Accordingly, a siphon can be used to draw swamp water to the deeper level of the sea bottom. In the right-hand diagram, the pump whirls the sea water so that it rises over the top of the pumping vessel, and the vacuum created by the rising water draws swamp water through the siphon that looks like a bent drinking straw. Leonardo noted that the sides of the vessel are sealed so that more water can enter it only through the siphon tube. The small sketch below shows that he took the human hand as a model for his pump agitator to whirl the water. At the center of his picture, he drew the details of the pump. The wheel directly above the vessel is a flywheel, one of Leonardo's favorite devices, which keeps the agitator turning at an even rate.

Leonardo's pump and the modern centrifugal pump both resemble a certain amusement-park ride: people lean against the sides of a large topless cone made of wood, and as the cone spins faster and faster, they find it increasingly difficult to continue leaning there. Centrifugal force whirls the people away from the cone just as it whirls the water away from the center of the pumping vessel. In the fifteenth century, power sources probably were not adequate to make such a pump really efficient, but the modern pump, run by any of several kinds of power, works so well that it is used even on fire engines. Our present-day centrifugal pumps have a spiral shape like the cross section of a snail shell. The inner section of the spiral whirls, and its vanes direct the water into the outer circle leading to the exit.

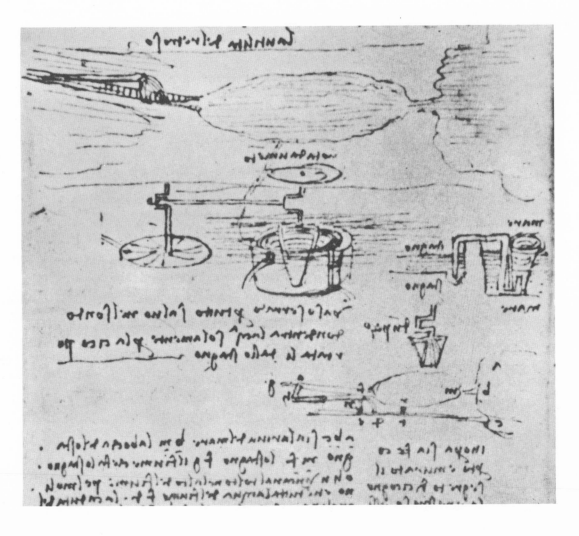

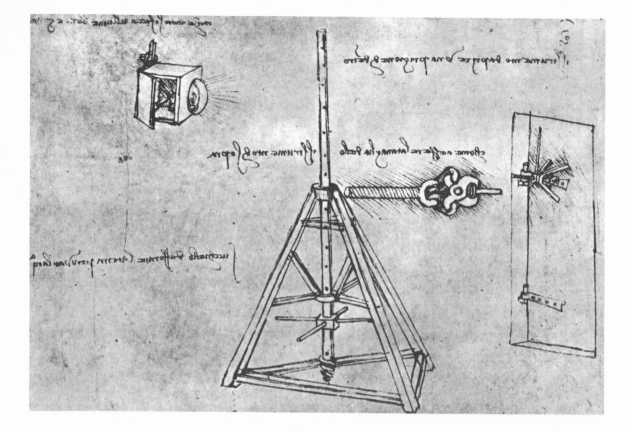

"TO DRILL INTO THE GROUND AND FIND WATER," Leonardo devised a screw attached to a long rod that was driven into the ground by turning the spokes near the bottom of the frame. The little dots on the rod are markings to show how deep the drill has gone, and the detail at the right shows how to lock the drill point in place. This process would be necessary very often, because the metals available in the fifteenth century would have worn down fast if turning against rock. At the far right, Leonardo seems to be applying his well-drill idea to the problem of removing the nails from a door hinge. There were no nail pullers in his day. The picture on the left illustrates Leonardo's projector (see section on Optics for details).

A system much like Leonardo's is the most recent technique for drilling artesian wells. Such drills, attached to a hollow pipe, easily go hundreds of feet into the ground; water forced down through the pipe brings up the rock dust dislodged by the drill. The machine is so constructed that the drill will have a larger diameter than the pipe, thus making a hole that leaves space around the pipe where the rock dust can rise to the surface of the ground. Oil drillers use the same method, except that oil drills may go thousands of feet down in order to find an oil deposit. They have been known to reach depths exceeding 20,000 feet. In oil drilling, a special kind of mud replaces the water used in drilling artesian wells. The new rotary system of drilling became possible only when very hard materials had been introduced to make the drill points, a fact that throws doubt on the practical value of Leonardo's machine.

AN EXPERIMENT WITH A BELLOWS FOR PUMPING WATER may have been Leonardo's idea in this drawing. Instead of the usual piston that forces water up the supply pipe as it descends, Leonardo seems to be using the bellows for this purpose. The bellows, marked by the two wavy lines down the middle of the sketch, surrounds the piston rod and is attached in such a way that a downstroke of the rod stretches the bellows; the effect is similar to what happens when you pull out an accordion from both ends. As the bellows stretches, it occupies more space than in its folded position, thus giving the water in the pump cylinder less space. The water has to go somewhere because it can't be compressed, and a valve system directs it upward and out the exit valve near the top of the cylinder, at the left. The domed arrangement on top appears to be a handle and a cone valve connecting with the piston rod; when the handle is pushed down, the point of the cone enters the ring and forces the rod down too.

In a force pump like this one, the whole cylinder remains at the bottom of the stream or well, so that a long rod would actually connect the handle and valve at the top with the cylinder itself, but Leonardo has squeezed them together on paper.

In the fifteenth century, people also used suction pumps to raise well water; this pump stays at the top of the well and draws water by creating a vacuum in the pipe leading from the pump to the well bottom. Its principle is the same as that of the barometer: normal air pressure on the water in the well forces the water into a partial vacuum just as normal air pressure forces liquid up the barometer tube. In Leonardo's day, people believed Aristotle's statement that a vacuum was immediately filled simply because "nature abhors a vacuum"; they didn't realize that air pressure caused the vacuum to be instantly filled. The suction pump is the kind that used to be worked by the handle on a kitchen sink before running water became a general convenience. Because it works by means of air pressure, it can be used to raise water only about 25 feet, while a force pump such as Leonardo installed to supply the Milan castle can raise water much higher.

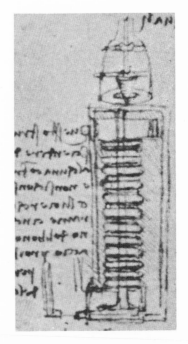

LEONARDO'S FLOATING DREDGE IS HELD BETWEEN TWO BARGES and operated by turning the crank marked *n*. The buckets at the end of the arms have little holes in them so that the water drains off but the mud stays inside them; as they revolve, they dump the loads of mud into two smaller barges placed between the large ones. Ropes from one barge to the stake marked *m* hold the barges in place. Leonardo seems to have intended this machine for swamp-clearing.

When the Ostrogoths laid siege to Rome in the sixth century, they cut off the aqueducts supplying water, leaving the Romans without power for the water wheels that turned their millstones. The Romans would have had no bread to eat if it hadn't occurred to them to set up floating mills in the river Tiber, which ran fast enough to turn the water wheels. They paired the boats, as Leonardo suggested for his dredge, put two mills on each boat, and set the water wheel between them. This successful scheme was probably the first use of floating machinery.

Some of our floating dredges now take the form of power-driven shovels with clamshell buckets, so called because of the way they open and close from a hinge. The dredge is mounted on a boat rather than being held between two barges by means of a pole, but the idea remains the same as Leonardo's.

To SIMPLIFY CANAL CONSTRUCTION in swampy ground, Leonardo invented a machine that would permit excavation to be done on two levels at once. If you look at this picture carefully, you will see that the crescent-shaped piece at the right is part of the machine. The light part of the crescent is level with the surface of the ground, while the darker part descends vertically from the surface to the lower level of excavation. The lines resembling tiny telegraph poles projecting from the top of the crescent indicate gates; when they are raised, as the picture illustrates, the swampy ground at the surface will flow through the gate openings into the boxes set in front of each opening on the level platform of the crescent. Down below, where the ground is firmer, another set of doors in the vertical face of the crescent may be opened so that men with pickaxes can remove the ground through them. A pickax rests against the wall next to the fourth door from the left. Thus the crescent not only provides for two crews of men to work on different levels but also acts as a huge

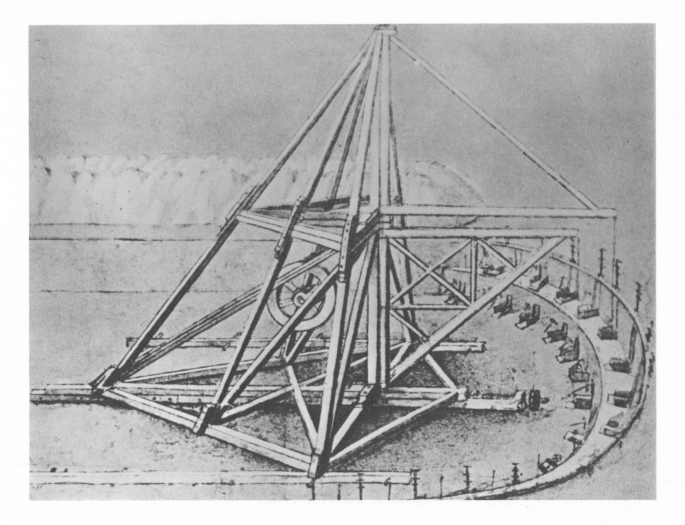

shield that prevents the swamp from flowing in again after the area has been cleared.

The wheel in the center of the machine operates two cranes, one at each level. One crane rises when the other drops, so that they counterbalance each other. The cranes remove the earth from the boxes and dump it on the pile resembling a mountain range behind the machine. As you can see, the dump pile extends as far as the excavating has been completed. But this machine has still another feature: it is mounted on three wooden tracks and can be moved forward to keep up with the work. A small wheel at the right-hand end of the middle track turns a worm gear to move the machine along; the tracks are probably made in sections, and the last section of each can be transferred to the front so as to extend the tracks when the machine needs to be advanced.

Of course this machine had to be enormous, and might have been impossible to build, but Leonardo had a very sensible idea when he designed it. Canal construction through rock is now done by blasting, and through soft ground with power shovels, but in his day canals were built by excavating a small stretch of ground at a time and placing a long series of wooden barriers at short intervals to prevent the cleared space from filling up again. His plan did away with the need for the barriers because the machine always provided the only barrier necessary as it moved along. A shield based on the same idea is sometimes used today for tunneling under rivers. It consists of a metal cylinder that can be advanced under the river as the tunnel-boring progresses; compressed air inside the cylinder prevents mud and water from entering while the men do their work. Leonardo would understand it very well.

"I BELIEVE I CAN COMPETE WITH ANYONE . . . in the building of canals," Leonardo wrote in a letter recommending himself to the Duke of Milan, and his excellence as a canal engineer is still remembered. He thought about everything, from the best way to dig the canal to the way water flowed through it and the best means of keeping the canal bottom and sides in good condition.

Here he suggests a plan for opening and closing lock gates. As you can see in the larger sketch, a series of locks in a canal acts like a flight of steps and in effect, permits ships to climb hills, while always traveling on a level canal between one lock and the next. The lock gates, placed at each end of the lock, can be closed to seal the ship

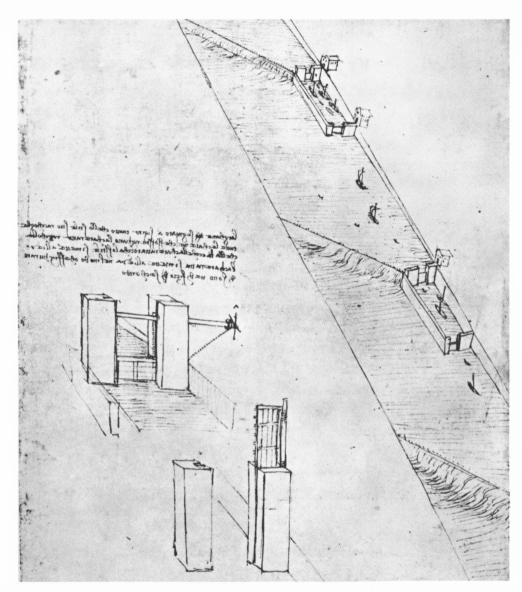

into the lock chamber so that the water level inside the chamber may be changed. Water is admitted through a sluice in the high-water gate to raise the ship, or released through the low-water gate to lower it. The ship has then gone up or down a water step and can proceed on the new level.

The small drawings at the left show one of Leonardo's methods of opening and closing the lock gate. In the upper sketch, he illustrates how chains connect the lock gate to a winch with a long shaft; turning the spokes of the winch handle winds the chains around the shaft and lifts the gate straight up. After the gate has been raised enough so that its top surface touches the winch shaft, the shaft is used as a lever: the lower sketch shows how the shaft moves from a level to an upright position to pivot the lock gate into the air and make room for the ship to pass through.

Some lock gates resemble double French doors that swing open and meet in the middle when closed. Leonardo realized that such gates should meet at a slight angle to make a shallow V facing upstream; in this arrangement, the force of the current running against them would keep them firmly closed and leakproof. These gates, he said, should be opened by pivoting them around a post against the lock wall. The modern method differs from his plan only in that power-driven machinery swings the gate.

Leonardo didn't invent lock gates, but his skill as an engineer improved them.

In his service for Duke Ludovico Sforza, Leonardo took charge of installing locks to connect the canals in the neighborhood of Milan. He would have admired the double locks of the Panama Canal that permit ships to go through in opposite directions at the same time. Each of these locks is about 1,000 feet long and takes an hour or so to fill or empty, but ships passing through the 40-mile Panama Canal save a journey of 8,000 miles around Cape Horn to go from the Atlantic to the Pacific.

"Let the dark, gloomy air be seen beaten by the rush of opposing winds wreathed in perpetual rain mingled with hail, and bearing hither and thither a vast network of the torn branches of trees mixed together with an infinite number of leaves." When he wrote these words, Leonardo was giving advice to the painter on how to represent a deluge; the painter could have been nobody but himself. He continues: "All around let there be seen ancient trees uprooted and torn in pieces by the fury of the wind. You should show how fragments of mountains, which have been already stripped bare by the rushing torrents, fall headlong into these very torrents and choke up the valleys, until the pent-up rivers rise in flood and cover the wide plains and their inhabitants. . . .

"Some groups of men you might have seen with weapons in their hands defending the tiny footholds that remained to them from the lions and wolves and beasts of prey which sought safety there. Ah, what dreadful tumults one heard resounding through the gloomy air, smitten by the fury of the thunder and the lightning it flashed forth which sped through it, bearing ruin, striking down whatever withstood its course! Ah, how many might you have seen stopping their ears with their hands in order to shut out the loud uproar caused through the darkened air by the fury of the winds mingled together with the rain, the thunder of the heavens and the raging of the thunderbolts! Others were not content to shut their eyes, but placing their hands over them, one above the other, would cover them more tightly in order not to see the pitiless slaughter made of the human race by the wrath of God."

Thus Leonardo, the genius of art and science, the man who could fathom many of nature's mysteries while never revealing his own, predicted that the mighty force of water would overpower man and bring his world to an end.

INDEX OF ILLUSTRATIONS

KEY

CA—Codex Atlanticus
CAr—Codex Arundel
CF—Codex Forster
CL—Codex Leicester
MS—Manuscript
W—Windsor Collection

Air-cooling machine (MS B 82r), 64
Anchor, undersea (CA 346r-a), 156
Anemometer (CA 249v-a), 106

Band brake, for millstone (MS L 34v), 128
Bell and hammer (CF II 10v), 31
Boat, paddle-wheel (CA 384r-b and IBM model), 135
Bomb, fin (W 12651), 150
Breathing tube (CAr 24v), 160
Bridge, two-level (MS B 23r), 137
Bridges, swing (CA 312r-a), 151

Canal, plan for (CA 33v-a), 173
Canal excavator (CA 1v-b), 171
Cannon, wheel-lock closure for breech-loading (CA 10v-a), 144
Cannon lighter (CA 56v-b), 145
Cannon-stave shaper (CA 2r-a), 73
Chains, sprocket (CA 357r-a), 123
Chariot, scythe (British Museum), 152
Church, plan for (MS B 24r), 40
City
    double-decker (MS B 36r), 43
    spindle-shaped (CA 217v-b-c), 41
Clock
    alarm (MS B 20v), 67
    with minute and hour hands (IBM model), 110; (CA 348v-d), 111
Coin stamper (CA 3r-a), 89
Columns, strength of (MS A 45r), 47
Compass, suspension for magnetic (CA 288r-b), 104
Compasses
    drafting (MS H 108v), 100
    proportional (CA 248r-a), 100
Copper-strip roller (MS B 70v), 72
Cord twister (CA 2v-b), 79
Costumes (W 12574-5), 35
Crane
    double (MS B 49v), 50
    hoisting (CA 49v-a), 49

"David," sculpture by Verrocchio, 4
Deluge, drawing (W 12380), 175
Diving suit (CA 333v-a), 155
Dredge, floating (MS E 75v), 170
Drum, mechanical (CA 335r-c and IBM model), 29

Earth's radius, method of measuring (MS A 20v), 103; (MS A 21r), 108

File-groove cutter (CA 6r-b), 83

Flying machine (MS B 74v and IBM model), 55
Flying saucer (MS B 80v), 58
Fortress, circular (CA 48r-a), 157

Gears, helical (CA 396r), 127
Glider, study (MS G 74r), 54
Glove, webbed (MS B 81v), 160
Gun
    machine (CA 56v-a), 143
    steam (MS B 33r and IBM model), 147
Gunpowder piston (MS F 16v), 130

Hands, study of (W 12558), 21
Hull borer (CA 333v-a), 155
Hulls, streamlined (MS G 50v), 134
Human figure, proportions of (Venice Academy of Fine Arts), 9
Hygrometer (Louvre), 24; (IBM model), 105

Imola, map of (W 12284), 92
Inclinometer (CA 381r-a), 102

Jack
    ratchet (CA 40r-a), 51
    screw (CA 49v-a), 51

Lamp, oil (MS B 80r-a), 66
Landing gear, study (MS B 89r), 57
"The Last Supper," figure sketches for (Louvre), 24
Lathe (CA 381r-b), 81
Lens grinders (CA 396v), 115
"Leonardo Dying in the Arms of Francis I," painting by Ingres, 19
Levels (W 12668), 46
Life preserver (CA 276v-a), 161
Lion, drawing (Louvre), 13
Lock gates (CA 33v-a), 173

Magnetic dip board (MS A 20v), 103
Mirror grinders (CA 396v), 115
Mortar-making tools (W 12668), 46
Mortars (CA 9v-a), 149
Motor, weight-driven (CA 8v-b), 126
Muscles, study of (Anatomical MS B 27r), 16

Nap-raiser (CA 38r-a), 77
Nap-shearer (CA 397r-a), 78
Needle grinder (CA 31v-a), 87

Odometer (CA 1r-a), 101

Parachute (CA 381v-a), 59
Pedometer (CA 1r-a), 101
Pipe borer
    horizontal (CA 393r), 84
    vertical (MS B 47v), 85
Piston, gunpowder (MS F 16v), 130
Pontine Marshes, map of (W 12684), 95
Printing press (CA 358r-b), 86

Projector (CA 9v-b), 116, 168
Pulley block (CA 396r), 122
Pump
    centrifugal (MS F 13r), 167
    force, with bellows (MS E 75r), 169
    water-supply (IBM model), 163

Ripples, study of (MS A 61r), 10
Roller bearings (IBM model), 122

Saw (CA 381r-b), 81
Scaffold, festival (MS B 28v), 34
Screw, aerial (MS B 83v), 61
Screw-thread cutter (MS G 70v), 74
Sforza horse monument, studies for (W 12321), 25
Shears, adjustable (CA 396r), 127
Ship, double-hull (MS B 11r), 153
Shoes, floating (CA 7r-a), 162
Shrapnel (MS B 31v), 148
Soil borer (MS B 65r), 68
Spectacles, man wearing (Quaderni d'Anatomia V 6r), 117
Spinning wheel (IBM model), 75; (CA 393v-a), 76
Spit, roasting (CA 5v-a), 65
Sprocket chains (CA 357r-a), 123
Stable, plan for (MS B 39r), 69
Stage, revolving (CAr #263 224v), 36; (IBM model), 37
Stairs, multiple (MS B 47r), 42
Star of Bethlehem, botanical study (W 12424), 7
Steam-expansion tester (CL 10r), 107
Sun, method of measuring distance to (MS A 21r), 108

Tank (British Museum), 152
Telescope, diagram (MS F 25r), 119
Transmission
    differential (IBM model), 124
    friction (IBM model), 124
    gear, three-speed (IBM model), 125
Trumpet, key (CAr 175r), 28
Turbine
    air (CA 13v-b), 131
    water (CAr 63v and IBM model), 129
Tuscany, map of (W 12683), 93

Valve, conical (IBM model), 166
"Vessel, mysterious" (MS B 11r), 153
Viol, mechanical (MS B 50v), 30

Wagon, horseless (CA 296r-a), 138; (IBM model), 139
Water, method of raising by means of fire (CA 7r-a), 162
Water-raising system (CA 401r-b), 165
Well drill (CA 9v-b), 168
Wire-strength tester (CA 82r-b), 48
World, map of (W), 97
Wrench, monkey (IBM model), 80

GENERAL INDEX

*Numbers in italic
indicate illustrations.*

Air, 10, 17, 24, 26, 41, 47, 52, 99, 104-105, 127, 132, 158, 161, 165, 166, 174, 175; air-cooling machine, 63, *64-65*; atmosphere, on moon, 90; and color, 113; compressed, 130-131, 139, 155, 172; for divers, 154-156, 160; drills, 131; as factor in flight, 52-61; friction, 65; and moisture content, 105; as power, 15, 51, 56, 61, 65, 66, 120, 121, 130-131, 139, 159; pressure, 12, 169; and projectiles, 141; supply for submarines, 154, 156; turbines, 121, 130-*131. See also* Weather, Wind
Air conditioning, modern, 65, 70; and fixed-speed motor, 127
Airplane, 52, 53, 54, 56, 57, 58, 61, 70, 94, 98, 102, 132, 134, 161; *Flyer,* 52; jet, 120; supersonic, 132. *See also* Flying machine
Alarm clock, 63, *67*
Alchemy, 16, 33, 76
America, 3, 26, 41, 63, 70, 72, 93, 94, 104, 132; Civil War, in 142, 145; as name on map, 20, 96; nineteenth-century theater in, 32; places in: Boston, 72; Kitty Hawk, N. C., 54; Mystic, Conn., 79, 104; Nantucket, 153; New England, woodcut map of, 96; New Jersey, 136; Philadelphia, 41, 136; Revolution in, 29, 136, 156. *See also* New York, Chicago.
Anatomy, 20; comparative, 25; drawings, 21, 94; human heart, 20; studies of: blood circulation, 159, eye, 113, muscles, *16,* proportions, 8, *9,* 22-23. *See also* Body, human
Anchor, undersea, *156*
Anemometer, *106*
Animals, 13, 22, 25, 112, 140, 174; bat, 52; bones of, 4; camel, 110; cat, 77; cod, 96; dinosaur, 60; dog, 3, 59, 65, 86; eagle, 52; elephant, 152; goat, 39; hedgehog, 77; Leonardo's attitude toward, 2; leopard, 35; lion, *13,* 35, 174, mechanical, 33; lizards and others, 33; mosquito, 94; nature's provision for, 2; ox, 135, 145; porpoise, 134; as power, 15, 71, 120, 135, 145; sea creatures, fossils, 11; skunk, 10-11; toads, as medicine, 16; wolf, 174. *See also* Horse
Arch, 41, 42; as support for weight, 45
Archimedes, 49
Architecture, 3, 19, 23, 37-43, 44, 63. *See also* Buildings, City planning, Construction
Aristotle, 91, *169*
Art, 21, 22, 24, 135, 175; European, 7; Leonardo's approach to, 4, 18, 21. *See also* Drawings, Painting

Assyrians, 161
Astrolabe, 17
Astronaut, 11, 90; *113,* 132
Astronomy, 3; instruments for, 99; star angles, 17
Atomic bomb, 140, 142; peace as defense against, 157
Atomic fission, 120
Autogiro, 61
Automation, 17, 70, 71, 82
Automobiles, 43, 51, 62, 70, 102, 130, 133, 134, 139; ball bearings in, 123; band brake in, 128; and differential transmission, 124-125; emergency gas tank in, 165; friction transmission in, 124; fuel-supply valve in, 166; gearshift in, 125; mile counter in, 102, 125; service stations for, 139, 165. *See also* Wagon, horseless
Aviation, 3, 52-61, 133; gliding, 52; and Maginot Line, 157. *See also* Flight

Babylon, hanging gardens of, 41
Bacon, Roger, 118
Balloons, 52, 59, 60
Barometer, 169
Basel, flying saucers in, 58-59
Bath, 62, 63; heating system for, 5
Beams, in nap-raising machine, 77; strength of, 45, 47-48, 136
Bearings, ball, 123; roller, 121, *122,* 123
Bellows, for air-cooling, 64; for air turbine, 130; for gunpowder piston, 130; for organ, 29; for pumping water, 169
Bells, 10; carillon, 31; with hammer, 30-*31*
Belt-drive, 79, 123
Bible, 12, 13
Birds, 11, 13; flight of, 52-57; Leonardo's attitude toward, 2; notebook on flight, 20; study of, 3, 5, 11, 134. *See also* Animals
Boats, 43, 127, 162, 170; barges, for floating dredge, 170, for pontoon bridge, 150; hydrofoil, 134; paddlewheel, 133, 134-*135;* steam, 133, 134-135; *The Steamboat,* 135; wineskin, 156. *See also* Ships
Bobbin, and spindle, 75-76
Body, human, 3, 10, 16, 159; bone structure, 16; circulation of blood, 159; eye, 16, 20; hair and hygrometer, 105; hand, as model for pump agitator, 166; heart, 16, 20; in art, 23; nerve systems, 16; study of proportions, 8, *9,* 22-23; tongues and vocal organs, 32
Bombs, 141; atomic, 140, 142, 157; missiles, modern, 141, 145, 149; with percussion cap, 150; stinkbomb, 3, 148; with tail fins, 141, *150. See also* Projectiles

Books, 6, 16, 20, 32, 86, 94, 135; arithmetic, 98; code, 91; geography, 90, 96; Leonardo's, on water, 158-159
Borers, hull, *155;* for soil, 68; for wooden pipes, *84, 85,* 86
Borgia, Cesare, 92, 140
Botany, 3; study of, 7. *See also* Plants
Bow, for mechanical viol, 30; as weapon: 142; crossbow, 51; for shooting bomb, 150
Brakes, air, 131; band, *128*
Bramante, Donato, 38, 40
Breathing tube, 142, 156, *160;* for altitude flight, 161; in life-jacket, 161
Bridges, Julius Caesar's, 151; lift, 151; for military use, 141, 150; pontoon, 150-*151;* strength of construction, 136; swing, 150-*151;* truss, 136; two-level, Chicago, 43; two-level, Leonardo's, 136, *137;* Verrazano-Narrows Bridge, 48-49
Brunelleschi, Filippo, 33, 38
Buildings, 5, 17, 35, 38, 39, 42, 44, 63, 79; castle, Milan, 162, 169; Leaning Tower of Pisa, 12; palaces, 5, 38, 39, 45, 91; prefabricated, 39; skyscrapers, 38, 44, 45; temples, Greek, 38. *See also* Churches, Fortifications
Buonarroti, Michelangelo, 23, 27, 40
Bushnell, David, 156

Cables, suspension-bridge, 48
Caesar, Julius, 151
Calorimeter, 107
Camera, photographic, 5, 94; television, in pipe making, 84-85, in weather reporting, 106
Camera obscura, 116-117
Canals, 20, 39, 41, 159; construction, 171-172; machinery for digging, 159; Panama, 174; and Pontine Marshes, 94-95; two-level excavator, *171-172. See also* Locks, canal
Cannon, 141, 149; balls, 141, 144; "Big Bertha," 73; breech-loading, *144-145, 148;* wheel-lock closure for, *144*-145; cage extension, for loading, 145; lighter for, *145;* manufacture, 72-73; staves, 72; on wheels, 145
Cardan's suspension, 104
Cayley, Sir George, 54
Cellini, Benvenuto, 19, 89
Chain, drive, 31, 123; hoists, 50; lift for lock gates, 173; sprocket, *123*
Chain hoists, and gears, 50
Charles VIII, of France, 145
Chicago, 42-43; Century of Progress fair, 44
Chinese, helicopter toy, 53, 60; kite, 54, 56; magnetic compass, 104; printing and paper, 86; Wan Hoo and flight, 56; wind carriage, 139

Church, 6; art, 22; music for, 26; opposition to dissection, 8

Churches, 5, 6, 38, 39, 40, 44, 45, 92; cathedrals, 23, 38-39, 44; Milan cathedral, 45; Pisa cathedral, 110; plans, 40-41; Riverside Church, 30-31; St. Peter's, 40; Santa Maria delle Grazie, 24, 38; "theater for preaching," 41

Churchill, Sir Winston, 152, 153

Cierva, Juan de la, 61

Cioni, Andrea di Michele di Francesco di, 4. See also Verrocchio, Andrea del

Circle, in band brake design, 128; in building design, 39, 40; drawing perfect circle, 100; and map of Imola, 92; in proportions of body study, 8; and self-registering instruments, 103-104; widening in ripples, 10

City, design and planning, 38, 39; double-decker city, 42, 43; imaginary cities, 92-93; Imola, 92; and maps, 91; spindle city, 41

Clocks, 30, 71, 98, 110-111, 126; alarm, 63, 67; atomic, 111; clockwork, 30, 110; with minute hand, 17, 110-111; sundial, 111; water clock (clepsydra), 111, 166; wrist watch, 17

Cloth, 71, 77; for costumes, 35; cotton, 77; drapery, painting of, 23; fabrics, modern, 62, 76, 80; linen, for aerial screw, 60, 61; for parachute, 59; manufacture: nap-raising, 77-78, nap-shearing, 78, and lawn mower, 78; spinning, 75-76, 121, weaving, 70; and optics experiment, 113; taffeta, for mechanical wings, 57; textiles, 70, 71; woolen, 77; yarn, 75-76, extrusion, 76

Clouds, 12; on stage, 33

Codex Arundel, 18, 20

Codex Atlanticus, 18

Codex Leicester, 18, 20

Coins, 88-89; abuses, 89, 99; milling, 87-88; stamping machine, 88, 89

Color, 22, 112; and distance, 113; distortion and projector, 117; and eye, 20; fringe and telescope, 116; Leonardo's study of, 113; in painting, 23; and sky, 113; and smoke, 113

Columbus, Christopher, 3, 17, 63, 90, 91, 96, 141

Columns, for pulpit, 41; strength of, 45, 47-48; as support in building, 44, 48

Compasses, as drafting instrument, 100; magnetic, 104; on gimbals, 104; and perfect circle, 100; proportional, 100

Computers, 70, 98

Construction, 38, 44-51, 146; building materials, 44, 46-47, strength of, 45, 47; canals, 159, 171-172; church, 40; measurement for, 17; safety in, 47-49; strut, for bridges, 136; theory of, 45. See also Fortifications

Copper-strip roller, 15, 71, 72, 89

Cord twister, 79, 80

Costumes, 5, 23, 32, 33, 35

Cranes, 45, 51; double, 50-51, 172; hammerhead, 51; hoisting, 15, 17; movable, on guide wire, 49-50; on stage, 32-33

Cupping glass, 129

Dams, 51, 91, 130

Deluge, 159; representation of, 174-175

Diet, 62-63; calorimeter, 107

Differential transmission, 124-125, 139

Distance, effect on color, 113; illusion of, on stage, 32-33; measure of, 17, 101, 103, 107-109, 110, 132; and ship's speed, 98

Divers, 141-142, 154-156, 160; air supply for, 154-156, 160; and military purposes, 160; pearl, 160; skindivers, 56, 154; suit for, 20, 142, 154, 155

Drawings, Leonardo's: 18; anatomical, 21, 94; city plans, 39; of deluge, 159, 175; draftsmanship, 16, 23, 126; early sketches, 15; of human heart, 20; Leonardo's approach to, 3, 5; of machinery, 21; of moving water, 21; and steam, 107; for "The Last Supper," 24

Drebbel, C. J., 154

Dredge, floating, 170

Drill, 68, 84-86; air-powered, 131; chuck, 84; to find oil, 85, 168-169; to find water, 168; lathe, 86; point, 84, 85, 168-169; undersea, 156

Drum, cylinder, 30, 64-65, 80, 128; and mine detection, 141, musical instrument, 27, 29, 30; for oil, 73; in revolver, 142

Duke of Milan. See Sforza, Ludovico

Earth, 11, 12, 17, 90, 106; and exploration, 132; and magnetism, 102-103; maps of, 20, 90-91, 96, 97; measurement of, 91, 99, 103, 109-110; weight of, 120

Electricity, and light, 67; as power, 15, 51, 62, 120, 128-129; and turbines, 120-121

Elevators, 44, 50-51

Engineering, 3, 4, 5; Leonardo as engineer, 40, canal, 172, 174, military, 140, 150, 152; and Robert Fulton, 135

Engines, automobile, 124, 125, 166; compressed air, 139; Diesel, 51, 131, 132; helicopter, 61; internal combustion, 15, 120-121, 130; railroad, 50; reaction, 120; steam, 107, 120-121, 128, 132; turbines, 120-121, 128-131

England, 20, 41, 54, 56, 89, 128, 135, 136, 139, 146, 156; places in: London, 56, Yarmouth, 135

Eratosthenes, 109-110

Experiment, in science, 12, 27

Eye, and color, 20; and light, 112; and

need for eyeglasses, 117; study of, 113-114; and vision, 112-113

Eyeglasses, 11, 112, 113, 117-118; and Roger Bacon, 118

Festivals, 23, 33, 34-35; pageants, 5, 26, 33, 37; scaffolding for, 34-35

File-groove cutter, 71, 82, 83

Fin bomb, 141, 150

Fire, 10, 39, 52, 63; and burning glass, 114; escape, 42; fireballs, 149; fire-grinding of lenses, 116; and igniting explosives, 145; as power, 162; and shrapnel, 148; and steam propulsion, 146; used to raise water, 162

Fire engines, 162-164, 167; and Hero of Alexandria, 162-164; names of, 162-164

Fish, as guide to boat design, 134

Flight, 3, 20, 52-61, 161; of birds, 11, 52-57; Cayley's study of, 54; Leonardo's study of, 53, 102, 133; by man, 52-61; notebook on bird flight, 20; safety in, 53, 60; on stage, 32

Florence, 2, 6, 8, 25, 27, 33, 34, 35, 38, 45, 63, 71, 90, 91, 92, 96, 159

Flyer spindle, 76

Flying machines, 52-61, 134; inclinometer for, 102; landing gear, 53, 56, 57; tail, 53; wing slots, 53. See also Glider, Helicopter, Parachute, Wings

Flying saucer, 58-59

Flywheel, 81, 167

Force, 14, 120; and moving weight, 132, 133

Fortifications, 23, 156; field fortifications, 141; floating fort, 135; fortress, 5, 39, 140-141, circular, 141, 156-157; Maginot Line, 157; and mine shafts, 141; underground, 149

Fortress, changing design of, 141; circular, 156-157; underground, 156-157

France, 19, 25; Institute of, 18; Revolution in, 136; places in: Amboise, 19; Normandy, 170; Paris, 2, 18, 73

Francis I, King of France, 19, 33

Franklin, Benjamin, 136

Friction, 121-123, 132; air, 65; and ball bearings, 123; and electricity, 67; and mechanical efficiency, 121-123; and power transmission, 124; and roller bearings, 122, 124; rolling and sliding, 123; study of, 121-123, 133

Fuel, charcoal, 146; coal, 50, 62, 70, 105, 129; gas, 62, 120; petroleum products, 120, gasoline, 132; solid, 120

Fulton, Robert, 134, 135

Furniture, 62-63, 70, 86; bed on gimbals, 104; piano lifted by pulleys, 122

Fusee, 30

Galilei, Galileo, 10, 12, 14, 49, 90, 99, 110-111, 112, 118-119

Gama, Vasco da, 90

Gatling, Richard J., 143

Gears, 15, 17, 65, 74, 78, 82, 84, 101, 102, 110, 114, 121, 134-135; cage, 29, 76, 126, 152; helical, 127; to increase power, 49-50, 122, 127; to reduce speed, 101, 127; sprocket, 123; three-speed transmission, 125; worm, 72, 133, 172

Genghis Khan, 140, 161

Geography, 96; atlas, 96; book, first, 90; and Eratosthenes, 109-110; and Paolo Toscanelli, 96

Geology, 3; and surveying, 103

Gherardini, Lisa ("Mona Lisa"), 27

Gimbals, 104

Glass, 44, 63, 66, 72, 116; drinking, 14; mirror, 72; stained, 23. See also Mirrors, Lenses

Gliders, 52, 53; Cayley's, 54; Wright brothers', 54

Globes, for lamps, 68; in sky, 59; as world maps, 90-91

God, 6, 11, 16, 175; "god from the machine," 32; gods, Greek and Roman, 35, 37, 38

Gravity, 12, 14, 52

Greeks, 12-13, 22, 32, 38, 49, 64, 77, 99, 106, 112, 151; definition of "machinery," 121; learning of, 6

Guericke, Otto van, 67

Gunpowder, 108, 140, 142; Leonardo's recipe for, 148; piston, 121, 129-130; as power source, 129-130, 142-143

Guns, 141, 142, 150; flintlock, 145; machine, 142-143, and ribaudequin, 142; revolver, 142; rifling of, 150; self-propelled, 73; on stage, 33; steam, 121, 141, 146, 147. See also Cannon

Hammer, 88; for bell, 30, 31; for file-groove cutter, 71, 82; mechanical, 89; for pile driver, 146

Handwriting, Leonardo's, 8, 18, 20

Hannibal, 152

Health, 16, 41, 42, 44; and city planning, 39; and cupping glass, 129; and diet, 62; and laser, 112; malaria and Pontine Marshes, 94; and microscope, 112; need for eyeglasses, 117

Heat, 11, 65; calorimeter, 107; and moisture, 105; rays of, 11

Helicopters, 20, 53, 60-61

Helix. See Screw, aerial

Hero of Alexandria, 162-164

Hitler, Adolf, 140

Holland, 139, 154

Home, 62-68; appliances, 62-63, 120, 124, 169; household expenses, 18; needles for, 88; and power, 120, 129

Horse, 18, 34-35, 39, 58, 68-69, 77, 124, 135, 140-141, 145, 150, 152, 164; bronze, 25; steam, 146

Hull borer, 155

Huygens, Christian, 110

Hydraulics, and drainage of Pontine Marshes, 94-95, swamp, 159; hy-draulic: lift, 50, power, 51, 57, screw, 128, 129, 159

Hygrometer, 24, 104-105

Ice, 62, 63, 107

Imola, map of city, 92

Inclinometer, 102

Industry, 70-89, 120-121; and business, American, 70; machines, 70-89; mass production, 71, 87-88

Inertia, 14

Ingres, Jean-Auguste-Dominique, 19

Instruments, for measuring, 17-18, 23, 24, 98-111; anemometer, 106; barometer, 169; calorimeter, 107; hygrometer, 24, 104-105; inclinometer, 102; magnetic dip board, 102-103; metronome, 110; mile counter, 102, 125; odometer, 17, 101; pedometer, 101-102; scale, 17, 99; sighting, 109; spoons, 23. See also Clocks, Compasses

Instruments, musical, 26-31; accordion, 168; angle chimes, 66; bassoons, 26; double-reed, 26; fife, 29; horn for diver, 154; lute, 27; music box, 27, 29, 65-66; oboes, 26; organ, 29. See also Bell, Drum, Trumpet, Viol, mechanical

Instruments, optical, 112-119; eyeglasses, 11, 112, 117-118; laser, 112; lens grinders, 114, 115, 116, 119; magnifying glass, 118; microscope, 112; projector, 116-117, 168; spyglass, 118. See also Telescope

Italy, 2, 6, 23, 63, 71, 104, 118, 120, 132-133, 135, 145, 158; places in: Bologna, 92, Naples, 94, 145, Pisa, 110, Pompeii, 77, Turin, 20, Tuscany, 91, 93, Venice, 154. See also Florence, Milan, Rome, Imola

Jacks, 45, 51; ratchet, 51; screw, 51

Julius II, Pope, 88

Kite, 54, 56

Kramer, Dr. Max O., 134

Lamp, 67; with adjustable base, 35; hanging, and Galileo, 110; oil, 63, 66-67

Laser, 112

"The Last Supper," 5, 23, 24, 38

Lathe, 74, 81-82; and crankshaft, 81, 121; drill, 86; treadle, 81

Lawn mower, and nap-shearing machine, 78

Lens grinders, 114, 115, 116; concave, 119; and friction, 122

Lenses, 47, 66; eyeglasses, 117-118; grinding of, 114-116, concave, 119; and magnification, 113-114, 117-119; projector, 116-117; and sky-watching, 114; telescope, 116, 118-119; toric, 66

Leonardo. See Vinci, Leonardo da

Levels, for construction, 46, 47

Lever, 17, 30, 37, 45, 68, 78, 120, 128, 149, 173

Life jacket, 161

Light, 20, 112-119, 152; and curved mirrors, 114; and electricity, 67, 120; in home, 63, 66-67; in Leonardo's landscape paintings, 7; Leonardo's study of, 113-114; lighting, stage, 23, 32-33; motion of, 10, 27, 113; photometry, 113; in stable, 69

Lighter, for cannon powder, 145

Lippershey, Hans, 118

Locks, canal, 172-173; double, 174; gates for, 159, 172, 173, 174, and current, 174

Machinery, 30, 51, 70, 71, 72, 73, 80, 82, 121, 127, 158, 159, 170, 174; floating, 170; and Greeks, 121; Leonardo's approach to design, 15, 49; Leonardo's drawings, 21; stage, 32-33, 37.

Machines, 2, 5, 15, 17, 120-121, 124, 158, 159; canal excavator, 171-172; cannon-stave shaper, 71, 72, 73; coin stamper, 89; copper-strip roller, 15, 71, 72, 89; cord twister, 79, 80; file-groove cutter, 71, 82, 83; floating dredge, 170; flying, 52-61; and friction, 122; for home, 62-68; industrial, 70-89, 121; for lifting, 45; nap-raising, 77-78; nap-shearing, 78; needle grinder, 71, 87; oil drills, 169; pile driver, 88, 146; printing press, 86-87; screw-thread cutter, 71, 74, 121; sewing machine, 88; spinning wheel, 70-71, 75-76, 121; tin roller, 71, 124; water-finding drills, 168-169. See also Engines, Instruments, Pumps, Tools

Magellan, Ferdinand, 90

Magic, 2, 8, 23, 32, 33, 76; spells and spirits, 32

Magnetic dip board, 102-103

Magnetism, 11, 102-103; and magnets, 27, 158

Manuscript A, 18

Manuscript B, 18

Maps, 90-96; bird's-eye view, 93-94; charts, 91; imaginary cities, 92-93; of Imola, 92; and Martin Wald-seemüller, 96; of moon, 90; of New England, 94; of Pontine Marshes, 94-95; projections, 96; relief, 20, 91, 94; three-dimensional, 94; of Tuscany, 93; weighted, 91; world, 20, 90-91, 96, 97

Mathematics, 3, 8, 10, 22, 104; binary system, 98; calculus, 98, 100; counting, 98; equations, 98, 109; geometric design, 39, 40; reckoning, 98; tables, 44

Measure, 16, 98-111; of altitude, 99; braccio, equivalent, 59, 98; of distance, 17, 101, 103, 107-109, 132; of earth, 91; of heat, 107; importance of, 17; instruments for, 17, 18, 23, 24, 98-111; of magnetic pole angle,

Measure (*continued*)
102-103; of moon, 90; of muscle power, 99; of speed, 98; of steam expansion, 107; and surveying, 99; of tilt, 102; of time, 110-111; variation in, 98; of weather, 17-18, 24, 99, 104-106, 169; of wire strength, 48

Mechanical advantage, 45, 120

Medici, 34-35; Lorenzo de' (the Magnificent), 27, 35; Palace, 91

Melzi, Francesco, 18

Metal, 71, 74, 82, 88, 106, 119, 146, 168, 172; reflecting mirrors, 114; rolling, 15, 71, 72; shaping, 71-73

Milan, 5, 18, 24, 25, 27, 38, 39, 41, 45, 71, 98, 159, 169, 174

Millstone, 71, 170; and band brake, 124; floating, 170

Mind, Leonardo on the finite, 10, 11, 13; of painters, 22

Mirrors, 22, 27, 72; curved, 67; grinding of, 114; Mirror John, 114; Mt. Palomar telescope, 116; reflecting telescope, 114-116

Models, built from Leonardo's sketches, 21

"Mona Lisa," 7, 19, 21, 27; theft and recovery of, 2

Monkey wrench, 71, *80*

Moon, 11, 52, 90; maps of, 90; seas and craters, 90

Mortar, as building material, 46; as weapon, 130, *149*; Great Mortar of Moscow, 149; Little David, 149; and trebuchet, 149

Motion, first law of, 14

Motor, 31, 130; and air drills, 131; airplane, 52; helicopter, 51; Leonardo's design for, *126-127*; for machine guns, 143

Mountains, 22, 95, 107-109, 120, 172; Alps, and Hannibal, 152; and deluge, 174; Leonardo's study of, 3, 11; and maps, 91, 93-94; measurement of altitude, 99; Mt. Palomar, 116; on stage, 33, 37

Muscles, *16*; measure of, 99; as power source, 15, 53, 54, 56

Museums, 18; Institute of France, 18; Louvre, 2, 19; Metropolitan, 4; Mystic, Conn., whaling museum, 79, 104; Windsor Collection, 18

Music, 3, 26, 27-31; instruments, musical, 26-31

Nap-raising machine, 71, 77, 78
Nap-shearing machine, *78*
Napoleon, 136
Nature, 2, 6, 8, 10, 14, 22, 112, 158, 169, 175; Leonardo's harmony with, 3; Leonardo's study of, 5, 11, 12, 13, 14, 15, 21
Navigation, 17, 104, 132
Needle grinder, 71, 87-88
New York, 4, 30, 48, 72, 93, 135, 156, 162
Newton, Sir Isaac, 14, 89, 114-116

Nobel, Immanuel, 161
Notebooks, Leonardo's, 18, 20, 74, 96, 104, 133; Codex Arundel, 18, 20; Codex Atlanticus, 18; Codex Leicester, 18, 20; on flight of birds, 20; MS A, MS B, 18; treatise on painting, 23
Notes, Leonardo's, 5, 8, 12, 14, 15, 18, 20, 45, 54, 72, 114, 159; fables, prophecies, riddles, 13; theoretical, on circle, 100
Nut, and bolt, 74, 80; and screw, 99; threading inside of wooden, 74

Observation, in science, 11-12
Ocean, 17, 158; Atlantic, 18, 90, 104, 132-133, 158, 174; and body's "pool of blood," 159; Pacific, 174
Odometer, *101*
Oil, crude, 85; drills for, 86, *168*-169
Optics, 3, 112-119; eye and colors, 20; instruments for, 11, 112, 114-119; study of, 113-114, 117, 118-119
Ostrogoths, 170

Paddle wheels, 133, 134-*135*
Paine, Tom, 136
Painting, 2, 3, 4, 5, 8, 19, 21, 22, 27, 33, 90; and deluge, 174-*175*; fresco, and weather, 24; and Robert Fulton, 135; at Pompeii, 77; "The Last Supper," 5, 23, 24; figure sketches for, 23, *24*; "Leonardo Dying in the Arms of Francis I," *19*; Leonardo's landscapes, 7; Leonardo's treatise on, 23; oil paints, 23; perspective, 22, 23; *sfumato*, 23
Palaces, 5, 38, 39, 45; Medici, 91
Paper, invention of, 86
Parachute, 11, 53, *59*-60
Paradise pageant, 35, 37
Pedometer, *101*, 102
Pendulum, and clocks, 110-111; and pedometer, 102
Penn, William, 41
Perkins, James, 146
Perspective, painting, 22-23; on maps, 92; on stage, 33
Perugia, Vincenzo, 2
Philosophy, 3; Leonardo as philosopher, 19; morals in Leonardo's notes, 13
Photography, 5, 21, 106; aerial, 94; telescopic, 90; television, 90
Photometry, 113
Pipes, boring machines, 84-86; of breathing tube, 160; making modern, 84-85; movement of water in, 158; pipelines, 84-85, 95; for plumbing, 38, 164-166; of pumps, 162, 169; to supply turbines, 128-129, 130; for well drills, 168
Piston, 82, 107; and bellows, in pump, 169; gunpowder, 121, 129-*130*; of pumps, 162
Pivot, 49, 100, 104, 151, 174
Planets, 52, 109; on stage, 37
Plants, 3, 22, 68; and deluge, 174;

flowers, 22; hanging gardens, 41; juniper, 34; leaf arrangement, 20; and light, 112; lilies, 33; Star of Bethlehem, lily, 7; teasel, part of thistle, 77-78; tool for pruning, 127
Plastics, 70
Plato, 91
Playing cards, and movable type, 86
Pliny, 160
Plumbline, 47, 99, 102, 103
Pontine Marshes, draining of, 94-95; map of, *94-95*
Posthole digger, *68*
Power, 15, 17, 30, 51, 52, 53, 54, 56, 68, 82, 86, 120-132, 134, 139; animal, 71, 120; electric, 120, 128-129, fixed-speed, 127; gasoline, 132; gunpowder combustion, 129-130, 142-143; hydraulic, 51, 57, 128; hydroelectric, 121, 129; manpower, 45, 64, 71, 120; mills, 128; nuclear, 121; rocket, 56, 146; station, 50; steam, 120, 139, 146; sources, 120-121, 127, 130-131, 167; and vacuum, 129-130. *See also* Air, Engines, Springs, Transmission of power, Water, Weight
Prefabrication of houses, 39
Printing, 70, 86-87
Printing press, 6, *86*-87; automatic feed for, 86-87; cylindrical, 87; flatbed, 86-87; and playing cards, 86; type for, 86
Projectiles, 149, 150; bullets, 145, 150; cannon ball, 141, 144, 146; fireballs, 149; iron balls, 146; shells, explosive, 73; shrapnel, 141, *148*; theory of, 141. *See also* Bombs
Projector, *116*, 117, *168*
Pulleys, 17, 18, 32, 37, 45, 49, 51, 53, 54, 65, 79, 87, 121, 138; fixed and movable, *122*; to increase power, 122
Pumps, 63, 107, 131; air-lift, 159; with bellows, *169*; centrifugal, 166-*167*; fire, as power, 162; and fire fighting, 162-164, 167; force, 162, *163*, *169*; kitchen, 62, 169; and siphon, 166; suction, 130, 169; system with "stork," 164, *165*; valves in, 164-166; water-supply, 159, 162, *163*; well, 17

Radio, 11, 26, 70; and television, 70, 72
Rafts, 161
Ratchet, 126; jack, *51*
Rays, 119; cosmic, 106; emission of, 10, 11; and laser, 112; light, 66-67, 113, and lenses, 118; sight, 112-113; sun, and measurement, 103, 109
Renaissance, 6, 22, 23, 33, 38, 40, 44, 152
Revere, Paul, 72
Rifling, of guns, 150
Ripples, circular, *10*, 11
Rivers, 2, 41, 42, 91, 93, 136, 158-159; of air, 12; Arno River, 159; Chicago River, 43; and deluge, 174; movement of, 158; Rhine River, 151;

Thames River, 154; Tiber River, 170; Tigris and Euphrates rivers, 158; tunneling under, 172

Rockets, as power, 56; steam, 146

Rocks, 4, 10, 11, 20, 149, 158; and canal construction, 172; and drilling, 168-169

Rollers, in industrial machines, 15, 71, 72, 76, 77, 78, 84, 87, 124; power, 72, 128; and power transmission, 124; roller bearings, 121, *122*, 123

Romans, 22, 32, 37, 41, 49, 77, 94-95, 120, 126, 141; and coinmaking, 89; and diver's breathing tube, 160; and floating mills, 170; and floating valve, 166; and measuring distance, 101; and paddle-wheel boat, 135

Rome, 40, 53, 94, 98, 114, 152, 170

Rope, 79-80, 82, 170; bridge, 150; and pulleys, 122; ropewalk, 79-80; and spring, as power, 81

Rope-twisting machine, 79, 80

Ropewalk, for making rope, 79-80

Russians, 85, 90, 146, 149

Safety, in construction, 47-49; in flight, 53-60; for roasting spit, 65

Sand, 47; as standard of measure, 48-49

Sanitation, 41, 63; privies, 39, 42; pure air, 41; sewage, 39, 42

Saws, 81-82; jigsaw, 82; mechanical, 71, *81-82*; rotary, 81; sawmill, 81-82

Scaffold, adjustable, 35; for festival, *34-35*

Scale, to read weights, 17

Scenery, 5, 23, 32-33, 34-35, 37

Science, 9, 12, 14, 15, 18, 20, 21, 22, 24, 132, 175; experiment in, 12; Leonardo's definition of, 18; Leonardo's study of, 3, 5, 11; observation in, 11-12; revival in Italy, 6; theory in, 12, 13, 14

Screw, 51, 68, 72, 74, 80, 84, 121, 127, 145, 146, 156; aerial, 53, 60, *61*; hydraulic, *129*; for lifting jack, 51; manufacture, 71, 74-75; and nut, 99; in turbine, 128; for water-finding drill, 168

Screw-thread cutter, 71, 74-75, 121

Sculpture, 19; Leonardo's opinion of sculptors, 27; Sforza monument, 25; statuary, 23, 38; statue of "David," *4*; Statue of Liberty, 42

Scythe chariot, *152*

Sea, 11, 42, 52, 91, 93, 94, 95, 142, 158, 159, 161, 166; Mediterranean, 104, 132, 158; seas on moon, 90; on stage, 33; and transportation, 132-133; undersea anchor, *156*

Sforza, Beatrice, Duchess of Milan, 5, 63, 64

Sforza, Ludovico, Duke of Milan, 5, 27, 35, 37, 45, 63, 140; canal locks for, 174; Leonardo's letter to, 140, 150, 172; monument for, 25; water-supply pump for, *162*

Sfumato, 23

Shears, automatic, 78

Shield, excavating, 172

Ships, 49, 50, 51, 52, 91, 102, 132-133, 134, 160; *Andrea Doria*, 153; and canal locks, 172-174; *Charles W. Morgan*, 104; and compasses, 104; *Constitution*, 72; design of, 133, 134, and fish, *134*; double-hull, *153*; importance of maps for, 91; *Mayflower*, 154; and measure of speed, 98; "mysterious vessel," 11, *153-154*; and navigation, 17, 104, 132; sailing, 52, 132-133, 141; *Stockholm*, 153; streamlined, 20, 133, 134; warships, 141-142. *See also* Boats, Submarine

Shrapnel, 141, *148*

Signals, semaphore, 136; smoke, 109; tunnels used for, 136

Sikorsky, Igor, 61

Sky, 12, 32, 115, 118; and telescope, 112, 114

Skyscrapers, 38, **44**; Frank Lloyd Wright's, 44

Snorkel, 154, 160

Sound, acoustics, 40; effects on stage, 33; and measurement, 101-102, 106; motion of, 10, 27; nature of, 27; of voice, human, 10, 26; noise: and deluge, 174-175, and helical gears, 127, and steam gun, 146

Spaceships, 11, 90, 113, 132

Speed, measurement of, 98

Spindle, 79; and bobbin, 75-76

Spinning wheel, 70-71, 75-76, 121; flyer, 75-76; and yarn, 75-76

Spits, for roasting, 65; heat-propelled, 63, 65, 121; mechanical, 65-66

Springs, 48, 78, 166; for mechanical drum, 29; as power source, 15, 17, 30, 53, 71, 81-82, 120, 138, 145

Spyglasses, 118

Square, in building design, 40; in city planning, 41; in proportions of body study, 8; and strength of construction, 136

Stable, 39, 68-69

Stage, 23, 32-37; festivals, 23, 26; pageants, 5, 26, 35; revolving stages, 32-33, 35, *36*, 37

Stairs, 45; and canal locks, 172; multiple, 39, *42*; spiral, 42; steps on acoustical church, 41

Star of Bethlehem, plant, 7

Stars, 17, 104, 114; North Star, 103, 109

Steam, boats, 133, 134-135; engine, 82, 107, 120-121, 128; expansion, 99, 107, 121; gun, 121, 141, 146, *147*; horse, 146; and pistons, 107; as power, 120, 146; rocket, 146; tricycle, 139; turbines, 129, 131

Stinkbomb, 3, *148*

Stone, 44, 47, 49, 122; blocks, 50-51; grinding, 128; and odometer, 102; troughs, 69

Streets, city, 39, 44; and drilling, 131; gridiron plan, 41; numbered, 93; two-level roads, 42-43

Submarine, 11, 142, 156; and C. J. Drebbel, 154; and David Bushnell, 156; and Leonardo's "mysterious vessel," 153-154; nuclear-powered, 121; and wheel-lock closure, 145

Sun, 10-11, 12, 59, 104, 112-113; and measurement, 103, 107, *108*, 109

Swamp drainage, 159; and centrifugal pump, 166-167; and floating dredge, 170; Pontine Marshes, 94-95

Swimming, 53, 154, 158, 160; floating shoes for, *162*; foot fins for, 160; life jacket, *161*; webbed glove for, *160*. *See also* Divers

Swinton, Sir Ernest, 152-153

Tanks, containing air, 56, 154-155; containing water, 159, 164-165; gasoline, emergency, 165; military, 73, 133, *152-153*, terminology for, 153

Teasels, 77, 78

Technology, 38, 95, 123; and industry, 70-71

Telephone, 38, 72

Telescope, 11, 90, 99, 112, 114-116, 118-*119*; and Hans Lippershey, 118; Mt. Palomar, 116; and photography, 90; reflecting, 114-116; refracting, 116

Television, 70, 72, 84-85, 112

Theory, in science, 12, 13, 14, 18

Time, 32, 49, 100, 111, 120; and clocks, 110-111, 166; divisibility of, 98; and metronome, 111; as standard of measure, 132

Tools, 17, 18, 70, 71, 77, 100, 127, 166; air-powered, 131; cannon lighter, *145*; and chuck, 84; cigarette lighter, 145; drills, 168-169; files, 82; for grasping, *127*; hammer, 30, 71, 82, 88; levels, *46*, 47; for making mortar, *46*; mechanical saw, 71, *81-82*; monkey wrench, 71, *80*; nail puller, 80; pantograph, 127; pickax, 141, 171; pipe borers, *84*, *85*, 86; pliers, 80; posthole digger, *68*; punch, 88; screwdriver, 74, *168*; transit, 47; treadle lathe, 74, *81-82*, 121. *See also* Instruments, Machines

Toscanelli, Paolo, 96

Traffic, 42, 49, 136, 150

Transmission, differential, *124-125*, 139; of motion, 101, 110, 121, 125-127, 134-135; of power, 15, 17, 65, 81, 120-127, 139; three-speed gear, *125*. *See also* Gears

Transportation, 124, 132-140; by air, 132-133; canals for, 41; diversion of Arno for, 159; horseless wagon, 17, 124, 133, *138-139*; by land, 132-133, 138-139; parachute for, 53, *59-60*; by sea, 132-133, 134-135. *See also* Airplane, Automobiles, Bridges, Flight, Ships, Vehicles, Wagon

Triangle, as mount for machine gun, 142; proportional, and measurement, 103, 109-110; in proportions of body study, 8; right, for screw-

Triangle (*continued*)
  thread cutting, 75; in scale design, 99; and strength of construction, 136; triangulation, 103; and world map projection, 96
Trumpets, 27, *28*, 29, 35
Truth, Leonardo on, 3; Leonardo's sense of, 10, 11
Turbines, 120, 128-129; air, 121, 130-*131*; steam, 129, 131; water, 121, 128-129, 131, 159
Turks, 6, 154
Tuscany, map of, 91, *93*
Type, movable, 86

Unidentified Flying Objects (UFO), 59
United Nations, 132; and atomic bomb, 140
Universe, Galileo's theories concerning the, 12; Leonardo's study of, 3; telescope provides new view of, 112
United States, 26, 70, 72, 145

Vacuum, and Aristotle, 169; and barometer, 169; cups in printing press, 87; and fire pump, 162; and power, 129-130; and siphon, 166; and suction pump, 130, 162, 169
Valves, 51, 156, 164-165, 169; flap, 162; floating, 69, 164-165, conical, *166*, 169; in trumpet, 28
Vegetius, 160
Vehicles, 42; bicycle, 123; boats, 43; buses, trucks, 43, 131, 136; carriages, 136; elevator, 44, 50-51; escalator, 42; scythe chariot, *152*; sled, 54, 145; spaceship, 11, 90, 113, 132; steam horse, 146; steam tricycle, 139; subway, 42, 43; tank, 73, 133, *152-153*; tractor, 54, 152; train, 131; wheelbarrow, 101; wind carriage, 139. *See also* Airplane, Automobile, Flying machine, Ship, Wagon
Verrazano-Narrows Bridge, 48-49
Verrocchio, Andrea del, 4, 15, 35
Vespucci, Amerigo, 90, 96
Vespucci, Bartolomeo, 96
Vikings, 104, 132
Vinci, Leonardo da (1452-1519), biographical facts: appearance and personality of, 2-3; birth of, 6; buried at Amboise, France, 19; death of, 6; early studies of, 2-5; in Florence, 6, 25, 27; in France, 19; and Francis I, King of France, 19, 33; lives in Milan, 25; in Verrocchio's studio, 4, 15, 35
Vinci, town of, 3, 4, 6
Viol, mechanical, *30*

Vitruvius, 37

Wacker, Charles, 42-43
Wagon, 17, 101, 122-123, 133; carts, 42, 124; and differential transmission, 124;
Wagon, horseless, 17, 124, 133, *138-139*
Waldseemüller, Martin, 96
Walls, attack and defense of, 141, 149; city, 39, 92; mortar for, 46; and round fortress, 156; weaknesses, in construction, 45
War, 140-157; American Civil, 142, 145; American Revolution, 29, 136; communications, 136, 140; Leonardo's attitude toward, 2, 73, 140; Leonardo's study of, 141; and maps, 91, 94; naval, 141-142, 153-156, 160; prisoners, 80; on stage, 32; strategy of, 140-141, 142; War of 1812, 135; World War, 1-11. *See also* Divers, Fortifications, Ships, Weapons
Washington, George, 156
Water, 14, 42, 46, 53, 64, 65, 66, 67, 69, 72, 90, 94, 105, 107, 112, 133, 142, 146, 150, 154, 156, 158-175; and civilization, 158; clock, 111, 166; dams, 50, 91, 130; destructive force of, 158-159, 174-175; evaporation of, 159; in home, 62-63, 165, 169; Leonardo's attitude toward, 158-159, 174-175; Leonardo's drawings of, 21; Leonardo's study of moving, 3, 5, 11, 12, 15, 133, 158-159; power, 15, 17, 71, 120, 121, 128-131, 158, 170; pressure, 159, 160, 164, 166; projects and maps, 91, 94-95; raising devices, 84, *162*; shoes and skis, *162*; as standard of measure, 49, 111; turbines, 121, 128-129, 131, 159; turbulence of, 5, 134; waves, 10, 161. *See also* Ocean, Pumps, Rivers, Sea, Steam, Transportation
Water wheels, 15, 17, 64, 71, 72, 81, 120-121, 128, 158, 162, 170; horizontal, 128; overshot, 128
Watt, James, 82, 121, 128
Waves, air and water, 10; light, 113; ripples, 10; and tempests, 161
Weapons, 2, 5, 140-160, 174; artillery, 141, 145; crossbow, 51; firearms, 142; mortar, 130, *149*; ram, 51; ribaudequin, 142; staves, 72; sword, 142; torpedo, 156; trebuchet, 149; underwater charges, 160. *See also* Bombs, Cannon, Guns, Projectiles, Ships
Weather, fog, 154; humidity and rainfall, 17, 105; lightning, 27, 120, 174; measurement of, 17-18, 24, 99,

104-106, 169; storms and rain, 32, 175; temperature, 90, 99; tempest, 161; thunder, 27, 33, 37, 120, 174, 175; Tiros satellite, 106; and water cycle, 159
Weight, 11, 17, 67, 79, 86, 88, 89, 99, 104, 106, 120, 121, 122, 149; counterweight, 50-51, 71; cranes for lifting, *49, 50*, 51; of ice, 107; lifting, in flight, 52, 53, 54, 56, 61; lifting, with jack, 51, with pulleys, 122, with gunpowder, 129-130; moving, and friction, 132, 133; as power, 15, 17, 30, 64, 65, 71, 82, 110, 120, 126; and stress, 45, 47; studies, of falling, 12, 14, and floating, 162; studies of lifting, 45; support for, in building, 44-45; support of, by wire and cables, 48-49
Wells, 17, 169; artesian, 168-169; drills for, *168-169*; oil, 168-169
Wheel-lock closure, for cannon, *144-145, 148*; for submarine hatch, 145
Wheels, 31, 37, 50, 54, 57, 70, 72, 78, 79, 82, 87-88, 106, 120-132, 144-145, 172; for armored tank, 152; axle, 122-123; for cannon, 145; and differential transmission, 124, 139; and distance traveled, 101-102; escape, 30, 110; flywheel, 81, 167; grinding, 114, 116; for mechanical drum, 29; paddle, 133, 134-135; pegged, 76, 126; potter's, 114; size, and efficiency, 133; turbine, 128, 130; wagon, 17, 101, 124, 133, 138-139. *See also* Water wheels
Winch, 37, 49, 50, 53, 56, 57, 58, 77, 88, 135, 146, 150, 173
Wind, 10, 12, 15, 22, 106, 112, 139, 174; carriage, 139; and deluge, 174-175; instruments, 26, *28*; and projectiles, 150; and sailing ships, 132; trade winds, 104; and water, 133, 158. *See also* Air
Windmills, 131, 139; as power, 120
Wings, of airplane, 53, 56, 98; of bat, 52; of birds, 52, 53; of flying machines, 52, 53, 54, 56, 58; mechanical, 3
Wire, 107; brushes, 78; for cable, 48; electric, 38, 72; in floating valve, 166; guide, for crane, 49; in key trumpet, 28; needles, 88; strength of, in construction, 48, 99
World War I, 73, 133, 140, 157
World War II, 94, 140, 149, 151, 157, 160
Wrench, monkey, 71, *80*
Wright, Frank Lloyd, 44, 45
Wright, Orville, 52, 54
Wright, Wilbur, 52, 54.